SCIENCE IN THE SIXTIES

The Tenth Anniversary AFOSR Scientific Seminar
June 1965

Edited by

DAVID L. ARM

DIRECTOR OF THE SEMINAR

Cosponsored by

THE UNIVERSITY OF NEW MEXICO
THE AIR FORCE MISSILE DEVELOPMENT CENTER
THE AIR FORCE OFFICE OF SCIENTIFIC RESEARCH

The Air Force Office Of Scientific Research
Is One Of The Major Components Of
The Office Of Aerospace Research
United States Air Force

Library of Congress Catalog Card Number: 65-28687

Preface

THIS VOLUME is a collection of articles which are based upon lectures presented at the Tenth Anniversary Air Force Office of Scientific Research Scientific Seminar, "Science in the Sixties," held at Cloudcroft, New Mexico in June 1965.

The AFOSR Scientific Seminars are unique. Leaders in the fields of science encompassed by AFOSR's areas of scientific interests depict current outstanding activities and research problems in their fields. The lectures are truly broad and must be intelligible to nonspecialists in each field, since they are presented to audiences which consist of scientifically sophisticated individuals with widely varying interests and backgrounds. They must offer not only information in a specific field, but ideas for interdisciplinary action as well.

This book does not pretend to be a publication of the proceedings of the seminar. Neither is it a collection of scientific articles which have been written for publication in one of the several learned journals. This collection does, however, indicate the state of the art in areas comprising the spectrum of scientific efforts being supported by the Air Force Office of Scientific Research.

The Seminar was sponsored by the Air Force Office of Scientific Research in cooperation with the University of New Mexico and the Air Force Missile Development Center.

D. L. A.

Washington, D. C.
November 1965

Contents

Introduction

DURING THE PERIOD 14-25 June 1965 the Air Force Office of Scientific Research conducted a unique seminar at Cloudcroft, New Mexico. Each of the sixteen distinguished scientific investigators who spoke at this seminar was chosen for his place on the knife edge of his particular area of research, where work was being done that would, in all likelihood, influence the course of science.

Among the seminar attendees were more than two hundred selected research, development, and administrative scientists and engineers of the Air Force, both civilian and military. Liberally sprinkled among this group were representatives of colleges and universities, other Federal agencies, and armed forces contractors in industry and other research institutions.

The focus in time was the mid-1960's, coincidentally the tenth anniversary of the Air Force Office of Scientific Research. AFOSR is the Air Force agency with responsibility for stimulating fundamental scientific investigation throughout the world in those aspects of the sciences that bear upon what are considered the central technological barriers to future development of Air Force operating capabilities.

The 1965 seminar was the first in the long Cloudcroft series to span a wide variety of sciences. Earlier seminars had concentrated on critical areas of special Air Force interests such as optics, cybernetics, and geophysics. The broader format seemed particularly desirable in view of the frequently asked question, "Where are we now, and where are we going, across the spectrum of the sciences today?"

AFOSR Seminar speakers traditionally are asked to speak informally rather than to read scientific papers, and to discuss aspects of their work that are far in advance of the tidying-up process that usually accompanies the preparation of such papers. In this way the AFOSR Seminar has been notably successful in providing close associations on an unhurried, casual basis, in an isolated location. The effect has been to provide a rich background to aid all of us in the Air Force who work to ensure that new science has a timely impact upon Air Force operations.

By the end of the seminar it was apparent that the interdisciplinary point of view had contributed an unusual perspective of the unity of science, and strong evidence of the cross-circulation of ideas across the disciplines. Speakers often referred to each other's research and made use of concepts described in earlier lectures.

It was also apparent that, despite the non-publishing tradition of past seminars, a volume based upon the presentations would greatly further a major objective of this seminar, wide and timely dissemination of new scientific information to potential users. Thus the idea for this volume took shape, to which the speakers would contribute an article, as general or as specific as they wished, highlighting major points which developed during their talks.

What has emerged vividly is the interlocking strength of seemingly disparate avenues of investigation in the sciences today, and the clear indication that great progress is often made in small steps occurring in a variety of ways. It is difficult to convey to a non-scientific audience the impossibility of predicting in advance how new knowledge in the sciences will be of direct benefit in the future. This volume illustrates the problem perfectly.

I can predict, however, that some future historian of science will point to this book and say that some of those important small steps are recorded here.

William J. Price

WILLIAM J. PRICE
Executive Director
Air Force Office of Scientific Research

I. Paths to the Sixties

A. HUNTER DUPREE

I. OVER THE DISTANT HORIZON:

THE DEVELOPMENT OF SCIENCE IN AMERICA TO 1940

THE HISTORIAN has a place speaking to a group of scientists because his view of the past can expand the experience of those making decisions for the future beyond their own immediate horizon. He cannot predict the future, nor can he by examining the past make discoveries yet undreamed of by the scientists in their own proper disciplines. Yet he can, by tracing the scientific ideas of the past, indicate something of the nature of science and how its leading ideas are formed. He can also, because science does not take place in a social and institutional vacuum, trace the development of those institutions which give scientific ideas their environment.

Those who belittle science in America because of the dearth of great names are likely to overlook entirely that half of American history in which the Atlantic shore of North America was a series of British colonies. However, the time span of the history of modern science and of American history are almost identical. Thomas Herriot, who accompanied Sir Walter Raleigh's ill-fated attempt to colonize Virginia, was a distinguished mathematician, one of the first followers of Copernicus in England and a correspondent of Kepler. From the time of the first settlements the question was not what the American colonies contributed to science but rather what science contributed to the structure of American civilization. The Puritans had a philosophically secure place for science, and many of their strongest intellects devoted a major part of their energy to

A. HUNTER DUPREE, Professor of History of the University of California at Berkeley, is now writing SCIENCE IN THE FEDERAL GOVERNMENT, 1940 TO 1960, *companion piece to the earlier work covering the years prior to 1940. He is a member of the Historical Advisory Committee of the National Aeronautics and Space Administration and has served as a consultant to the Committee on Science and Public Policy of the National Academy of Sciences.*

investigating natural phenomena. Thomas Brattle made astronomical observations which were used by Isaac Newton in his *Principia*. The brightest ornaments of the American Enlightenment, Benjamin Franklin and David Rittenhouse, made contributions to political philosophy at least in part because of the positions they had gained in the transatlantic world through natural philosophy. Thus, from the very beginning American civilization gave a place of honor to science and developed differently because of its presence.

With the achievement of independence, the men of the early republic attempted to express their nationalism in science as well as in literature and art. The attempt to establish an American prime meridian to replace that of Greenwich was a characteristic gesture of the first generation. Almost immediately two basic attitudes toward the relation of science to American democracy became apparent. On the one hand, many, including Joseph Priestly, saw the free institutions established by the American Revolution as providing the essential condition of freedom in which science could be expected to flourish. On the other hand, some, such as John Quincy Adams, chided Americans for not providing support for science which the monarchies supplied as aristocratic patrons. In contrast to the numerous and well-endowed astronomical observatories of Europe, where were the "lighthouses of the skies" in the American republic? Thus the belief that an authoritarian state has a positive advantage in supporting science has been a part of the American's assumption about science for a long time, and the reactions to Sputnik I show that the idea is still very much with us.

Against such a background the United States, in the period after 1830, faced up to the problem of institution-building for science in the nation. In an age of seeming indifference to basic research, scientists could not admit in theory that they were building national scientific institutions. They had to pretend the Coast Survey was a temporary task force and not a permanent government agency. They had to introduce a national astronomical observatory in the guise of a Depot of Charts and Instruments for the Navy. It took an entirely unexpected bequest to bring the Smithsonian Institution into existence. Only the unusual political conditions of the Civil War period made possible the founding of a national academy of sciences. Not until late in the nineteenth century did the characteristics of universities, as we know them today, begin to take shape in the United States.

One important nineteenth century institution which has been almost eclipsed by the subsequent rise of the laboratory was the exploring and surveying expedition. These joint military-civilian enterprises not only were mounted to achieve very practical and specific ends but they also were major contributors to basic science across a wide band of disciplines. To take just one example, the botany of New Mexico was brought into the purview of international science within a few years after 1846 because civilian collectors, representatives of the leading botanists of the day, accompanied the troops which came to the area with the outbreak of the Mexican War. Augustus Fendler came with a detachment of the Army along the route of the Santa Fe Trail. Charles Wright reached El Paso with a military wagon train shortly afterward. The Mexican Boundary Surveys which followed on the Treaty of Guadaloupe Hidalgo and the railroad surveys of the mid-1850's brought more collectors to the region as part of civilian-military teams manned on the Army side by a group which specialized in scientific exploration— the Corps of Topographical Engineers.

After the Civil War the exploring and surveying expedition as a scientific institution tended to break up. This change enables one to speak of the decline of science in the military in the late nineteenth century without implying that a weapons-oriented research establishment would not be rising in the twentieth century. The replacement of the rival surveys of the 1870's—some of them military—with the permanent civilian scientific agency, the United States Geological Survey, makes 1879 a landmark date in the shift. The transfer of meteorological research from the Army Signal Corps to the Department of Agriculture in 1890 is a similar indication of the change.

With the dawn of the twentieth century, a spate of articles appeared bemoaning the state of basic science in America as compared to western Europe. Yet the very discussion of supposed American inferiority was an indication that American science was maturing. The growth of laboratories and of universities with their specialized departments as we know them today provided the characteristic locus of scientific activity in place of the exploring and surveying expedition. The dominant place which biology had achieved among the disciplines in the wake of the Darwinian revolution became attenuated by the rise of chemistry and to a lesser degree physics as the most prestigious sciences.

World War I was a major shock to American science. Even in 1914 the realization dawned that the United States had remained deeply dependent upon Europe not only for ideas but also for applications, particularly in the fields of chemistry and optical glass. The technical services of the American military had to begin their effort to apply science to twentieth-century weaponry from a standing start. Under the aegis of the National Research Council, created in 1916, American science reoriented itself into the pattern which foreshadowed its military role after 1940. Yet World War I was for American scientists an incomplete experience. And the most farseeing leaders were looking beyond the war itself even before American entry in 1917. George Ellery Hale had an international objective in mind in establishing the National Research Council. American leadership was important in setting up the International Research Council—the precursor of ICSU, the International Council of Scientific Unions—just as the nation as a whole was withdrawing from international cooperative action in the League of Nations.

In the inter-war years between 1920 and 1940 the scientific community in the United States took on characteristics which people, not considered old, can still remember, and which some—especially those who think that the deprivations of an economic depression strengthen character—look back upon as a golden age. An unnoticed contrast underlay the appearance of an international scientific community and the reality of increasingly nationalistic foundations for science support. Because communication across national boundaries became easy in the 1920's, many scientists could fancy themselves men who knew no nation but their own scientific discipline. Yet the rise of Hitler was to demonstrate how fragile the international community actually was.

In the United States the four sectors of science support within the nation achieved both balance and a clear division of labor. The universities, industry, the government, and the private foundations had some sense of the role to be played both by themselves and by the others. The universities were the home of advanced training and basic research. Industry provided a home for applied research in laboratories organized and financed by corporations. The government supported more research in absolute terms than ever, but it limited itself to supporting its own missions by investigations done in laboratories within its own walls. The private foundations, grown large on the concentrations of wealth put together in the late nineteenth century, played a major facilitating role in the government and university sectors, as well as mounting research efforts in directly-supported laboratories. Alone of the four sectors, the foundations had significant ties with the other three. The bonds between the government and the universities were particularly weak.

In the late 1930's American science showed its maturity by providing opportunities for the refugees coming over from the shadow of Naziism. These men recognized earlier, and more clearly than most, both the involvement of American science as such in the crisis and the need for binding the sectors of support together in a single great establishment directed to national ends.

II. THE FOREGROUND

A HISTORIAN'S REFLECTIONS ON AMERICAN SCIENCE SINCE 1940

The Office of Scientific Research and Development—the OSRD—was the nearest thing to a true central science organization in all of American history. In binding together all the sectors of science support in the immediate interest of the war effort it incidentally created a new system of American science. Its binding of the universities and industrial research to the government has continued even after the demise of the agency itself. The four major leaders of the OSRD—Vannevar Bush, James B. Conant, Frank B. Jewett, and Karl T. Compton—gained their extraordinary hold over American science not because of their personal qualities—however impressive these were—but because among them they represented all the major interests in American science and had standing in all the sectors. The decisions hammered out by the OSRD became precedents which shaped the structure of American science. The contract not only brought the universities and industrial laboratories into the service of the government but defined many important roles, such as that of the contracting institution and of the principal investigator. It established the principle of no loss and no gain for non-profit contractors and thus incidentally created the necessity for determining indirect costs. It determined the concentration and dispersion both of personnel and facilities purely on the basis of need, thus bequeathing both a geographical imbalance of research facilities and a rationale for continuing it on the postwar structure. It adopted a posture of independence from the military but in practice carefully geared itself to the needs of weaponry, not to basic research. Nothing illustrates more clearly the administrative ingenuity of the OSRD than the skill with which it spun off the Manhattan Project to the Army without at the same time losing touch with it.

At the end of the war in 1945, as the accomplishments of the scientists came into view, science policy divided itself into two spheres. The one which immediately engaged the attention of the whole world was the sphere of atomic energy. This policy area has its own dynamic which stemmed from its problem—the bomb. Hence it had its own relation to international policy, national policy, and to science. It had its own laboratories—the national laboratories— and its system of scientific information. It even had its own organized loyal opposition, a role played by a segment of the scientific community. The great storms of this policy area arose over the creation of a national atomic energy agency and over international control.

All of the excitement over the McMahon Bill and Baruch Plan tended to obscure, however, the other great sphere of science policy, the development of a national system of government science support in all the sectors. The Bush report, *Science, the Endless Frontier,* put forward in July 1945, just before the atomic explosion near Alamogordo, contained a plan for a comprehensive national science agency. Its national research foundation not only provided for government support of basic research in the universities by using the techniques of the OSRD; but it also envisaged medical and military research support under the same roof. Without the priority of the atomic energy policy area, legislation for a National Science Foundation failed of passage in 1946, and the opportunity of the reconversion period passed.

In place of a comprehensive foundation a variety of agencies created a multiple system of support by applying the methods of the defunct OSRD to basic research. The National Institutes of Health got a start as the primary locus of medical research with the help of the OSRD's medical contracts, which were transferred from the Committee on Medical Research. The military, organized after 1947 into the Department of Defense with its own Research and Development Board, found it necessary to support basic research in the universities at the same time that it strove to keep its in-house laboratories alive for weapons problems. The Office of Naval Research and its counterparts in the Army and Air Force had firmly established the pattern of support for basic research in the universities long before the National Science Foundation, shorn of some of the functions envisaged for it in 1945, came into existence in 1950, after five years of legislative maneuver.

By the opening of the 1960's it had become apparent that the new national system of science support was a permanent feature of American life, and people began to ask the question, "How has science fared under it?" The myriad answers which have been given tend to exhibit either an optimistic or a pessimistic tendency. The optimists point not only to the accomplishments in nuclear physics, but also to those in biology and medicine and nearly every other discipline, and say, "What I have seen in the past twenty years!" The great number of scientists, their equipment, their publications, make the United States the metropolis of one of the great ages in the whole history of science.

Those who take the gloomy view, on the other hand, fear that creativity has gone out of big science. The team and the factory atmosphere seem to the pessimists to have lowered the position of the scientist and sapped his individuality. Science has, by the very opulence of its support and by the confinement that comes with practical missions for research, been corrupted. Large projects can grind out expected answers in any detail desired, but the soaring generalizations of a Newton and a Darwin are no longer possible.

A line of research that is peculiarly characteristic of the age of the national system of research is the space effort. It is necessarily a huge team effort, and basic research is essentially dependent on technology to make the probing of space above the earth's atmosphere possible at all. Hence a corollary of the gloomy view is that American science made a wrong turn for political, which means in this context unworthy, reasons when it went strongly for space research and especially when it committed itself to manned space flight. Indeed, most of space flight is not science but technology, and though it has a value for science, the cost both in money and manpower is completely disproportionate.

One reason for this widely held judgment is that the scientific community has, since the late nineteenth century, come to think of itself not as engaging in exploration but in research. It has come to consider the essential home of science as the laboratory, forgetting in the accomplishments of controlled experiment that many of science's great triumphs of the past took place within the tradition of the exploring and surveying expeditions.

The true precedent for space exploration in several past centuries was the probing of the great reaches of the Pacific Ocean which lay south of the latitude of Acapulco—the route of the Manila galleon—and between the coast of South America and the East Indies. A little was known of the area from the time of Magellan, but the delivery systems, the ships, were so near the limit of their capabilities that the technology of just getting there from Western Europe and getting back took up nearly all of resources alloted to the exploration. Only in the eighteenth century, when the scientific corps was organized as a separate entity on the major expeditions, did research in the South Pacific area begin to yield data for basic research across a spread of disciplines in both the physical and biological sciences. The military was still necessary not only to provide escort but also to furnish scientific skill unavailable from civilian sources. The technological side of the combination remained important. Indeed, one of the most intractable problems lay in the field of guidance systems—how to determine longitude. And the military in general remained in command. The few times when scientists such as Edmund Halley were placed in command of naval vessels turned out to be disasters. Captain James Cook was quite capable of leaving Sir Joseph Banks at home when the scientist required alterations to the ship to accommodate his cabinet which impaired the sailing qualities of the *Endeavour*.

In one sense the late eighteenth century marked the culmination of the multi-discipline exploration of the South Pacific space. Captain Cook carried out his mission of contributing to the worldwide network of observation posts for the twice-in-a-lifetime opportunity to see and measure the transits of Venus across the face of the sun. He exploded the myth of a great southern continent extending its promontories into low latitudes and offering commercial and military possibilities. Banks and others contributed to the knowledge of the flora and fauna and geology of a vast segment of the earth.

Yet the deeper meanings of the data which the great expeditions collected largely escaped Cook's generation. In the 1830's a surveying ship, working alone and virtually without adventure to mop up the details of geography and hydrography of the area, *H. M. S. Beagle,* managed to occasion one of the major breakthroughs in the whole history of science. Charles Darwin had the insights which led to his theory of organic evolution while visiting the Galapagos Islands, but the data on which his work ultimately rested was the work of many generations of explorers who made it possible to correlate the distribution of plants and animals with the geology of continents and islands. The age of Cook, some of whose reasons for supporting space research were rewarded with only negative results, could not foresee the work of Darwin as the finest fruit of their investment.

Thus if space research is considered not as an unwelcome departure from the laboratory tradition but rather as an extension of the multidiscipline surveying and exploring expedition so familiar in the nineteenth century, it can be seen to have a continuity with the past. The necessity to adapt the experiment to the technology of the delivery system is not a new thing. The participation of the military and the requirements of command were familiar to scientists of another day. The joining of practical missions to basic research and curiosity concerning the unknown was quite familiar to Cook and Bougainville. Although the same disciplines are not involved in quite the same mixture, exploration has long been a team effort both among disciplines and between scientists and practical men. The demand that major results be predictable before the effort can be judged scientifically worthwhile can be no more met today than to have expected Captain Cook to predict the theories of Darwin. We are at the beginning of a new age of exploration.

II. The Concept of Mathematics Historically Surveyed

MORRIS KLINE

INTRODUCTION

I PROPOSE TO present not the latest technical results but rather a broad account of the nature of mathematics and of its relation to science as we understand these matters today. By the nature of mathematics I mean the very concept of a unique subject called mathematics, presumably distinct from any other scientific or humanistic corpus. Two distinguishing characteristics of mathematics have been accepted in the past as paramount. The first is its methodology and the second is its claim to truth. Its subject matter is also different from that of other fields but I shall not consider this feature. I propose to show you that the logic has always been in a somewhat sorry state and never more so than today. And I shall also show you that there isn't a word of truth in mathematics. Moreover, at the present time the status of mathematics as a distinct subject is so unclear that the mathematical and scientific worlds face a dilemma, a dilemma which threatens the very existence of mathematics and poses grave questions for science.

I believe it will be most helpful to adopt a historical approach. Apart from some interesting facts about the history itself, this approach will enable us to see how the traditional concept of mathematics arose, to what extent it has been correct, and what recent events have forced a reevaluation.

THE BABYLONIAN AND EGYPTIAN PERIOD

The phenomenon of mathematics is found in just a few of the

MORRIS KLINE is Professor of Mathematics and Director, Division of Electromagnetic Research at the Courant Institute of Mathematical Sciences, New York University. He is an AFOSR grantee. Dr. Kline is the author of numerous books, research articles and popular pieces on mathematics.

hundreds of earlier civilizations, Egypt, Babylonia and China. I shall ignore the development in China primarily because it had no influence on the main stream of activity. As for Egypt and Babylonia the mathematics that did exist there from about 4000 B.C. to 300 B.C., consisted of some simple arithmetic, the beginnings of algebra and a few geometric rules for finding the perimeters, areas and volumes of simple figures. One can hardly say that there was a subject called mathematics which was pursued as a distinct body of thought. All of the mathematics was just a handy tool to make calculations needed in construction projects, taxation, commercial transactions and agriculture. The concepts were drawn directly from experience and the conclusions were a collection of empirical rules and procedures which produced the desired quantities and which worked.

The Classical Greek Period

The people who created mathematics in the sense in which it is commonly understood were the Greeks of the classical period, the period from 600 to 300 B.C. The first great contribution of the Greeks was to supply the logical structure of mathematics. They insisted that all proofs of mathematical formulas, procedures, and assertions must be deductive. Thus, Euclidean geometry, which is one of the masterworks of the classical Greeks, is presented deductively. The great virtue of deductive proof is that the conclusions are unquestionable if one accepts the premises. The belief that mathematical conclusions are unassailable derives from the use of deductive proof.

It is important to appreciate how radical the insistence on deductive proof was. Suppose a scientist should measure the sum of the angles of a hundred different triangles, in different locations and of different sizes and shapes, and find that the sum is 180 degrees to within the limits of experimental accuracy. Surely he would conclude that the sum of the angles of any triangle is 180 degrees. But his proof would not be deductive and would not therefore be mathematically acceptable. Likewise one can test as many even numbers as he pleases and he will find that each is a sum of two prime numbers. But this test is not a deductive proof and so the result is not a theorem of mathematics. Deductive proof is, then, a very stringent requirement.

But the Greeks were after far more than impeccable proofs. They sought truths, especially truths about the universe. Since they believed that the universe is mathematically designed, a belief epitomized in Plato's "God eternally geometrizes," the truths about the universe would be mathematical. How could one obtain these truths? If one could start the chain of deductive proofs with premises or axioms that were truths, then, since deductive reasoning gives necessary consequences, these, too, would be truths. Fortunately the Greeks readily obtained some self-evident truths which served as axioms. It was self-evident that two points determine a line, that all right angles are equal, that equals added to equals give equals, and so on. From these truths they deduced others. Thus the second great distinguishing feature of mathematics was established. Mathematics gives truth about the universe. At the same time the relationship to science was established. Mathematics became part of the scientific effort to understand the physical world.

The Greeks insisted on the rigorous establishment of mathematics from self-evident truths. But they ran into a major difficulty. In the course of their work on number and geometry the Pythagoreans, a famous group of mathematician-philosophers, encountered irrational numbers. These arose through the application of the Pythagorean theorem itself, which says that the square of the hypotenuse of a right triangle equals the sum of the squares of the sides. Thus if the sides are each 1 unit long then the length of the hypotenuse is $\sqrt{2}$, and such numbers, as the Pythagoreans proved, cannot be expressed as a ratio of whole numbers. Now the Egyptians and the Babylonians had encountered square roots and with no further thought approximated them. But the Greeks were more meticulous. To them numbers meant whole numbers and ratios of whole numbers and since $\sqrt{2}$ was neither, it could not be a number. The Greek resolution of this difficulty was to refuse to recognize irrationals, such as $\sqrt{2}$, $\sqrt[3]{2}$, and $\sqrt{5}$ as numbers but to treat them as lengths, areas and volumes. Thus if one states the Pythagorean theorem as the square *on* the hypotenuse of a right triangle equals the sum of the squares *on* the other two sides, one has a statement about areas of geometrical figures in which no numbers enter. Consequently, though whole numbers and ratios of whole numbers were treated arithmetically the main body of classical Greek mathematics become geometrical.

The Alexandrian Greek World

The character and even the location of the Greek culture was drastically altered in the last quarter of the fourth century B.C. by the conquests and maneuvers of Alexander the Great. After he had conquered Greece, Egypt and the Near East, he decided to found a new capital for his world and he and his successors built the city of Alexandria in Egypt. There the classical Greek and the older Egyptian and Babylonian civilizations merged.

The classical Greeks had sought to understand nature but they were satisfied with the qualitative understanding which geometry afforded. The practical uses of mathematics in construction, navigation, calendar reckoning, commerce and finance were of no interest to these philosopher-mathematicians. However, the Alexandrians, influenced by the more practically minded Egyptians and Babylonians, put the sciences to use. In the Alexandrian period a quantitative astronomy applicable and applied to calendar-reckoning, the measurement of time and navigation was developed and, in fact, culminated in the remarkably accurate Ptolemaic theory. Mechanical devices, applied optics, geography, pneumatics and hydrostatics were pursued.

Applied science and engineering must be quantitative. When a ship at sea wishes to know its location, it wishes to know it numerically in terms of degrees of latitude and longitude. To construct effectively buildings, bridges, ships and dams one must know the quantitative measures of lengths, areas, volumes and masses to be employed so that the parts will fit nicely; in fact this quantitative knowledge must usually be obtained before the construction is undertaken. And so we find in Alexandria that the geometry was devoted to the derivation of algebraic formulas for lengths, areas, and volumes. To develop a quantitative astronomy Hipparchus and Ptolemy had to create trigonometry, which consists of geometry and algebra. Hence arithmetic and algebra assumed equal importance with geometry.

But the arithmetic and algebra, which were taken over from the Egyptians and the Babylonians, had no logical foundation. The Alexandrian Greeks adopted the Egyptian and Babylonian attitude. Irrational numbers such as π, $\sqrt{2}$, $\sqrt{3}$ and the like were used uncritically and approximated where necessary. The mathematicians, notably Heron, Hipparchus, Ptolemy and even Archimedes, did not hesitate to use irrationals freely. Thus algebra, which is of course no more than generalized arithmetic, was revived as an empirical science.

The content of mathematics now comprised geometry and algebra. Though the geometry still dominated, the algebra was no longer negligible. Moreover, from the standpoint of the logic, the situation was peculiar. The geometry was deductive and rigorously founded on self-evident axioms. The arithmetic and algebra were based on intuitive and empirical grounds. And despite the sharply different bases for these several subjects the classical Greek conviction that mathematics is truth about the quantitative and geometrical behavior of nature still prevailed.

THE HINDU AND ARABIC CONTRIBUTIONS

The Alexandrian Greek civilization was wiped out by Roman, Christian and Moslem destroyers, and the torch of mathematics was taken up by the Hindus and the Arabs, both of whom learned much from the Greeks. We shall not take the time to discuss these civilizations in detail. The significant mathematical developments are the Hindu contributions of zero and negative numbers.

From the standpoint of the logic of mathematics the outstanding fact is that both peoples worked freely with all types of numbers, particularly irrational and negative numbers, by relying upon intuitive and physical arguments or by reasoning by analogy. For example, since $\sqrt{9} \cdot \sqrt{16} = \sqrt{144}$, the Hindus and Arabs did not hesitate to state that $\sqrt{2} \cdot \sqrt{3} = \sqrt{6}$. The willingness of these people, somewhat like the Egyptians and Babylonians, to be guided by heuristic arguments is striking because it shows again how the civilization determines the character of the mathematics. By this time, roughly 1000 A.D., algebra certainly competed with geometry in extent and so we face the peculiar situation that about half of mathematics was rigorously established while the other half remained a series of rules and procedures with no logical basis.

THE RENAISSANCE AND EARLY SEVENTEENTH CENTURY

Through a series of historical events which we cannot trace here the European civilization not only was established but also acquired the Hindu, Arabic and Greek mathematics, the deductive geometry and the empirical algebra. By 1500 Europe was equipped to make contributions of its own.

The Europeans had the same difficulties in grasping the irrational number which the classical Greeks experienced and had the additional complication of absorbing negative numbers. Their perplexity in the case of the irrationals is well illustrated by the following remarks of Michael Stifel, a prominent German algebraist of the 16th century. He is considering irrationals as decimals and says: "Since, in proving geometrical figures, when rational numbers fail us irrational numbers take their place and prove exactly those things which rational numbers could not prove, . . . we are moved and compelled to assert that they truly are numbers, compelled, that is, by the results which follow from their use—results which we perceive to be real, certain, and constant. On the other hand, other considerations compel us to deny that irrational numbers are numbers at all. To wit, when we seek to subject them to numeration [decimals] . . . we find that they flee away perpetually, so that not one of them can be apprehended precisely in itself. . . . Now that cannot be called a true number which is of such nature that it lacks precision. . . . Therefore, just as an infinite number is not a number, so an irrational number is not a true number, but lies hidden in a cloud of infinity." Then Stifel argues that real numbers are either whole numbers or fractions and obviously irrationals are neither; hence they are not real numbers. In the seventeenth century Blaise Pascal and Isaac Barrow said that, for example, $\sqrt{3}$ can be only a geometric magnitude. Irrational numbers have no existence independent of continuous geometric magnitude.

Negative numbers were equally incomprehensible. Stifel called negative numbers absurd and the first great European algebraist, Jerome Cardan, called them fictitious. Francois Vieta, the founder of modern algebra, rejected them and René Descartes called negative roots of equations false. All sorts of arguments were given even as late as the eighteenth century to show that negative numbers make no sense.

To cap these troubles Cardan in his famous formula for the solution of third degree equations introduced complex numbers. He remarks that they are "sophistic quantities which, though ingenious, were useless," despite the fact that when the roots are real and distinct they are still given by cube roots of complex numbers. The algebraist Raphael Bombelli called complex numbers senseless while Descartes coined the term imaginary numbers, which indicated his opinion of them. Even Isaac Newton did not regard complex numbers as significant because they had no physical meaning. As in the case of negative numbers and irrational numbers all sorts of arguments were given to show the meaninglessness of complex numbers.

But the Europeans had to reckon with science. From about the year 1500 onward science and the application of scientific knowledge to engineering, navigation, military affairs, industry and social problems began to dominate the European civilization. Even in the sixteenth century the activity in astronomy, highlighted by the work of Copernicus and Kepler, the problems raised by the great explorations, the work in optics stimulated by the invention of the telescope and microscope, the study of projectile motion in behalf of the increasing use of cannons, and the investigation of magnetism loomed large in the European scene. The relevance of the vast expansion of science for our subject is that effective scientific work, particularly applied science, as we noted in connection with the Alexandrian Greeks, calls for quantitative knowledge. In addition, a new concept of scientific method, formulated by Galileo and most fruitfully applied by Newton, called for the description of physical phenomena by means of functions and the study of these phenomena by mathematical work with functions. This methodolgy of course put primary emphasis on quantitative relationships.

To cope with the growing scientific activity the mathematicians not only used irrational, negative and complex numbers but put forth new creations in arithmetic and algebra. This was the period in which logarithms were created to speed up the calculations of astronomers. In this period the main body of the algebra taught in our high school and elementary college courses was created by Cardan, Nicolo Tartaglia, Vieta, Descartes, Pierre de Fermat, John Wallis, and many others. And in this period also Descartes and Fermat created analytic or coordinate geometry in which curves are represented by algebraic equations in two variables so that the study of properties of curves could be pursued by algebraic techniques. With this creation the positions of algebra and geometry were reversed. Conclusions about geometry were to be established by algebraic reasoning.

The significance of the new mathematical developments is that algebra began to outstrip geometry. Since there was no logical foundation for algebra and since in particular negative numbers, irrational numbers and now even complex numbers had no clear definitions, to say nothing of any justification for operations with them, the logical structure of mathematics was in a sad state. Indeed many mathematicians, notably Pascal and Barrow, protested against the use of algebra because the logical foundations were not established. The philosopher Hobbes called algebra "a scab of symbols." Nevertheless, the mathematicians used arithmetic and algebra freely on a pragmatic basis. The rules gave physically correct results and this is what decided the issue for the time being. The needs of science prevailed over logical scruples.

THE RISE OF ANALYSIS

The logic of mathematics was thrown into a state of crisis by still further developments. The major scientific activity of the late seventeenth and the eighteenth centuries was the study of motion, particularly celestial mechanics. To carry on the study of motion, the notion of a function or formula, which is a relation between two arithmetically valued variables, is basic. Powerful methods of deducing and working with functions, notably the calculus, were created.

The basic concept of the calculus is the instantaneous rate of change of a function, namely, the limit of $\Delta y/\Delta x$ as Δx approaches 0. Isaac Newton, who shares with Gottfried Leibniz the honor of creating the calculus, thought of the limit in question, which is now called the derivative, as a velocity, which is the case when y represents distance and t, time, and he made great use of this fact in solving physical problems. But Newton experienced, for him, insuperable difficulties in explaining how he obtained the derivative from $\Delta y/\Delta x$. The difficulty lay in the fact that Δy also approaches 0 when Δx does and it seemed impossible to explain how such a quotient approached a definite number. Newton wrote three papers on the calculus and put out three editions of his famous *Mathematical Principles of Natural Philosophy* and in each of these publications he made different explanations. In his first paper he says that this method is "shortly explained rather than accurately demonstrated." In his second paper he changes some terminology so as "to remove the harshness from the doctrine of indivisibles" but the logic is no more perspicious. In the third paper Newton says "in mathematics minutest errors are not to be neglected." And then he gives a definition of the derivative, or fluxion as he called it, which supposedly shows that a fluxion is a precise concept. "Fluxions are, as near as we please, as the increments of fluents generated in times, as equal and as small as possible, and to speak accurately, they are in the prime ratio of nascent increments; yet they can be expressed by any lines whatever, which are proportional to them."

In the first and third editions of the *Principles* Newton says, "Ultimate ratios in which quantities vanish, are not, strictly speaking, ratios of ultimate quantities, but limits to which the ratios of these quantities decreasing without limit, approach, and which, though they can come nearer than any given difference whatever, they can neither pass over nor attain before the quantities have diminished indefinitely." He says, further, "by the ultimate ratio of evanescent quantities is to be understood the ratio of the quantities, not before they vanish, nor after, but that with which they vanish." There are other statements by Newton in the published versions of his works which differ from the above. Clearly Newton struggled hard to define the derivative but scarcely succeeded in formulating a precise concept.

Leibniz worked not with the ratio $\Delta y/\Delta x$ and its limit but with differentials dx and dy which, he said, though not zero were not ordinary numbers. They were geometrically the differences in abscissa and ordinate, respectively, of two "infinitely near points." He too published many papers in which he tried to explain the meaning of the ratio dy/dx, the equivalent of Newton's derivative. Concerning a paper published in 1684 even his friends, the Bernoulli brothers, said it was "an enigma rather than an explication."

Other papers and efforts to clarify his ideas did not accomplish any more. In a letter to Wallis, Leibniz says: "It is useful to consider quantities infinitely small such that when their ratio is sought, they may not be considered zero but which are rejected as often as they occur with quantities incomparably greater. Thus if we have x + dx, dx is rejected. But it is different if we seek the difference between x + dx and x. Similarly we cannot have xdx and dx dx standing together. Hence if we are to differentiate xy we write (x + dx) (y + dy) — xy = x dy + y dx + dx dy. But here dx dy is to be rejected as incomparably less than x dy + y dx. Thus in any particular case, the error is less than any finite quantity."

In the absence of satisfactory definitions he resorted to analogies to explain his differentials. At one time he referred to dy and dx as momentary increments or as vanishing or incipient magnitudes. These are Newtonian phrases. Then he says that as a point adds nothing to a line so differentials of higher order, e.g., dx dx, add nothing to dx. Then he says dx is to x as a point to the Earth or as the radius of the Earth to that of the heavens. There are many other statements by Leibniz which are equally obscure.

There were many attacks on Leibniz's and Newton's work. Newton did not respond but Leibniz did. The answers given by Leibniz show the state of affairs. Leibniz objected to "overprecise critics" and that we should not be led by excessive scrupulousness to reject the fruits of invention. The phrases infinitely large and infinitely small signify no more than quantities which one can take as great or as small as one wishes. And then he argues that one can use these ultimate quantities, the actual infinite and the infinitely small, as a tool much as the algebraists use the imaginary with great profit. He also said that if one prefers to reject infinitely small quantities, it was possible instead to assume them to be as small as one judges necessary in order that they should be incomparable and that the error produced should be of no consequence, or less than any given magnitude.

With these vague, unclear, almost impenetrable concepts serving to introduce a brand new branch of mathematics one would expect either that the whole subject would be dropped by mathematicians who boast of their precise reasoning, their indisputable conclusions, and the like, or that some genius of the order of Newton and Leibniz would come along and clear up the confusion in the subject. But neither step was made. Newton and Leibniz made correct and highly significant applications of their ideas and their successors not only retained what these inventors contributed but also added to the calculus, differential equations, infinite series, the calculus of variations and a host of other branches, now comprising what is called analysis, and made many more applications.

In the eighteenth century the attacks on the soundness of analysis generally continued and, in fact, were persistent. The most vigorous attack was made by George Berkeley, a bishop and philosopher, in his tract called *The Analyst*. The subtitle of this tract is interesting: *On a Discourse Addressed to an Infidel Mathematician* [Edmund Halley]. *Wherein it is Examined Whether the Object, Principles, and Inferences of the Modern Analysis are More Distinctly Conceived, or More Evidently Deduced, than Religious Mysteries and Points of Faith. "First Cast the Beam out of Thine Own Eye; and Then Shalt Thou See Clearly to Cast Out the Mote Out of Thy Brother's Eye."* Berkeley's description of dy/dx as the ghost of departed quantities is famous.

Because it was impossible to give a sound explanation of the calculus d'Alembert advised students of the subject, "Persist and faith will come to you." Berkeley and most mathematicians of the 18th century such as Euler, Lagrange, and Carnot, believed that the calculus worked because errors were somehow compensating each other. All of these men tried to build a sound foundation for the calculus and failed.

The upshot of the entire development of mathematics until 1800 is that by far the largest part of mathematics now rested on arithmetic and algebra rather than on geometry, and there was no logical foundation for this major portion. Nevertheless because the mathematicians and physicists thought in physical terms and used physical arguments to supply the deficiencies in mathematical reasoning, the application of mathematics to the study of nature attained enormous success. The most impressive results were obtained in the study of the motions of the planets and the earth's moon. Predictions of planetary and lunar positions reached the accuracy of fractions of a second.

And so we find a highly paradoxical state of affairs. The logic of the now vastly expanded mathematics was never in a sorrier state. But the success of mathematics in representing and predicting the ways of nature was so impressive that mathematics was securely established as a body of truths. More so than the Greeks, the intellectuals of the eighteenth century Age of Reason proclaimed the mathematical design of nature. The eighteenth century has been called the heroic age in mathematics because the mathematicians dared and achieved such magnificent scientific conquests on the basis of so little logical armament.

THE GREAT DEBACLE

The most significant development of the nineteenth century from the standpoint of the logical nature and the truth of mathematics was non-Euclidean geometry. It is not necessary for us to investigate the activity which led to this creation but we should note just what it offered. The basic fact about non-Euclidean geometry is that it is possible to adopt a different set of axioms from Euclid's and construct a body of theorems differing from those in Euclid. The key difference in the axioms is the parallel axiom. In place of assuming as Euclid did that through a given point in a plane there is one and only one line which does not meet a given line, one can assume that there are many such lines through the point or that there are none. The consequences of adopting a different axiom on parallel lines are weighty. For example, instead of the sum of the angles of a triangle adding up to 180 degrees, they add up to less than or more than 180 degrees. Another weighty consequence is that the distinction between similar and congruent triangles is wiped out. Two similar triangles must be congruent.

The very fact that there could be geometries alternative to Euclid's was in itself a shock to mathematics. But the consequences of the creation of non-Euclidean geometry were far more drastic. The first was that in the course of the work on non-Euclidean geometry the logic of Euclidean geometry was found to be woefully deficient. Euclid had given many meaningless definitions, had failed to define a number of the concepts he did use, and, worst of all, had used unconsciously any number of axioms that he never mentioned. To put it bluntly the logical structure of Euclid was seen to be terribly inadequate.

So, from the standpoint of rigor, by 1830 or so mathematics was in a desperate state. In view of the tremendous advances in analysis in the late seventeenth, eighteenth and early nineteenth centuries, ninety-five per cent of mathematics, everything built on arithmetic, had never had any logical foundation. Now the only piece of ground which had been assumed to be solid, Euclidean geometry, was found to be marsh land.

The Loss of Truth

Non-Euclidean geometry initiated the destruction of another foundation stone of mathematics—its truth. The man who was chiefly responsible for the creation of non-Euclidean geometry, Karl Gauss, realized at once that the new geometries might be applicable to the physical world and soon convinced himself that any one of them could be used. In other words, to within the accuracy of observation and measurement, physical space could be described by any one of several geometries. If several geometries, which contradict each other in part at least, can describe physical space then surely we do not know what is true about physical space. All one can say is that if we believe space has the properties of the axioms of Euclidean geometry or of one of the non-Euclidean geometries, then mathematics will tell us the consequences of our belief. Gauss thereupon concluded that geometry was part of mechanics.

Non-Euclidean geometry, a triumph of reason, paved the way for an intellectual disaster. It certainly showed that geometry does not offer truths. For a while the mathematicians, including Gauss himself, turned to arithmetic, algebra and analysis and said that the truth of mathematics rests there. But in the nineteenth century new algebras were created, an algebra of quaternions, an algebra of vectors, and an algebra of matrices. What is significant about these algebras is that they do not obey all of the laws of ordinary arithmetic. For example, the multiplication of two quaternions or of two matrices is generally not commutative. Consequently mathematicians began to realize that there is not just one algebra but many algebras just as there are many geometries. The situation is not quite the same in the two fields because the algebra of ordinary numbers was not changed. However, it became clear that this algebra too was man-made and that there was no assurance that its laws applied to the physical world. And in fact they need not.

Thus if one mixes two cubic centimeters of hydrogen gas and one cubic centimeter of oxygen gas one does not obtain three cubic centimeters of water vapor but only two. And if one combines one quart of rye and one quart of vermouth one does not get two quarts of alcohol but somewhat less. There is no guarantee, in other words, that the familiar arithmetic necessarily applies to the physical world. Thus algebra and arithmetic, too, are not truths.

Non-Euclidean geometry was a victory which almost cost the life of mathematics. The claim to truth about the physical world and rigorous proof, the two distinguishing features of mathematics, were both seen to be fanciful. What did preserve the life of mathematics was the powerful medicine it had itself concocted—the enormous achievements in celestial mechanics, acoustics, fluid dynamics, the strength of materials, optics, electricity and magnetism, and the many branches of engineering, and the incredible accuracy of its predictions. There had to be some essential, perhaps magical, power in a subject which, though it had fought under the protection of the invincible banner of truth, had actually achieved its victories through some inner mysterious strength. The extraordinary applicability of mathematics to nature remained to be explained but no one could deny the fact itself and dare to throw away such an all-powerful tool. And so mathematics retained its place in the intellectual and scientific worlds.

The Restoration of Rigor

But the mathematicians were not content. Their prestige was at stake. What was, henceforth, to distinguish lofty minded, noble-thinking mathematicians from earth-grubbing scientists? It was not possible to restore truth to mathematics. This gem was lost forever. But it might be possible to restore the rigor of proof to geometry and to instill rigor in the development of arithmetic, algebra and analysis.

The mathematicians of the nineteenth century did provide the rigorous logical foundations of their subject. A movement called the critical movement and initiated by the work of Bernard Bolzano and Augustin-Louis Cauchy and carried forward by Karl Weierstrass, Richard Dedekind, George Cantor, G. Peano and others provided for the first time an axiomatic basis for arithmetic, algebra and analysis. And Mortiz Pasch, David Hilbert and others supplied an improved axiomatic basis for Euclidean and the other geometries. In the course of this foundational work Cantor, who found himself obliged to treat various collections of points and numbers, created a branch of mathematics about which one hears much today—the theory of sets. In any case by 1900 the strict logical basis of mathematics was perfected. At a congress of mathematicians in Paris in 1900, Henri Poincaré boasted: "Today we may say that perfect rigor has been attained."

THE CONSISTENCY PROBLEM AND THE PARADOXES

The story of the development of the concept of mathematics would have had a happy ending if indeed it did end here. The satisfaction which mathematicians were enjoying from the newly attained perfect state of mathematics was short-lived. Mathematics now consisted of a set of rather arbitrary deductive structures each resting on axioms. These structures were no longer truths and hence the question arose, "How do we know that these structures are consistent, that is, that we shall not arrive at contradictions?" Previously the supposed truth of mathematics had guaranteed consistency, for truth by its very nature could not contain contradictions.

The problem of establishing consistency was aggravated by the discovery that mathematicians had indeed been using concepts which were self contradictory. And these contradictions were discovered in the very branch of mathematics that was created to rigorize the subject namely, set theory. The contradictions are called paradoxes, a euphemism which avoids facing the truth. I shall give some examples of these paradoxes in non-technical settings just to avoid the need to present any mathematical background. However, the examples are typical of mathematical counterparts.

The first of these paradoxes is called the barber paradox. A barber in a town boasts that he shaves all those people who do not shave themselves but of course he does not shave those people who do shave themselves. Should he shave himself? Clearly, if he does, he shouldn't and if he doesn't, he should.

Another example is the famous Russell Paradox. A class of books is not a book but a class of ideas is an idea. Hence some classes do not belong to themselves and some do. Denote by M, the class of all classes which are members of themselves, and by N, the class of all classes which are not members of themselves. M and N are clearly mutually exclusive but together include all classes. Now N itself is a class. Does it belong to M or N? If N belongs to N, it is a class which belongs to itself and so should belong to M. If N belongs to M, then it does not belong to N, since M and N are mutually exclusive. If N does not belong to N, that is, if N does not belong to itself, then by the definition of N, it should belong to N.

Finally let us consider the word "paradox." Each number is describable in many ways by words. Thus five can be described by the single word "five" or by the phrase "the next integer after four." Take the description involving the least number of letters and call this the minimum description. Consider now all numbers which are describable with 100 letters or fewer of the English alphabet. At most 27^{100} descriptions are possible and even if each is a minimum description there is at most a finite number of numbers describable with all 27^{100} descriptions. There must then be some numbers not described by the 27^{100} descriptions. Consider "the smallest number not describable in 100 letters or less." This number has just been described in less than 100 letters.

Thus the problem of establishing the consistency of mathematics was no longer academic. The paradoxes showed that mathematics was not consistent, and the problem of resolving the paradoxes and establishing the consistency of mathematics became imperative.

I might add that the nature of these paradoxes is that an object is defined in terms of a class of objects which includes the object defined. It is easy to overlook this circularity in making definitions. Thus suppose one defines the set S to be the collection of all sets each of which is definable in a statement of 25 or fewer words. Now S itself has just been defined in a statement of fewer than 25 words so that S is included in the class of sets by which S is defined.

THE MODERN PHILOSOPHIES OF MATHEMATICS

Three major philosophies have been developed, each of which seeks to resolve the difficulties just described. These are called the logistic, the formalist, and the intuitionist philosophies. I shall not try to do more than sketch the essential points in these philosophies.

The logistic school, led by Gottlob Frege, Bertrand Russell and Alfred North Whitehead builds up mathematics deductively from logic. Logic itself starts with axioms about propositions or statements and then is itself built up deductively. Then, with no further axioms, the concepts of mathematics and their properties are deduced. The development is a lengthy one.

To avoid the paradoxes Russell and Whitehead had to distinguish types of propositions. The purpose of this theory of types is to make sure that a propositional function of any one type does not apply to a set of objects containing that propositional function. This avoids defining an element in terms of a set which contains that element. But the theory of types introduced complications. To overcome them Russell and Whitehead introduced an axiom of reducibility to the effect that for each relation of whatever type among individual objects there exists an equivalent relation of simple type. The axiom is artificial and has no intuitive content.

There are several objections to this logistic approach. The first is that the consistency of the set of axioms used for logic, particularly in view of the artificial, non-intuitive axiom of reducibility, is open. Up to 1900, Russell believed that the principles of logic were truths but he soon realized that there was no basis for the belief. The second objection is that the deduction of mathematics from logic, which has no affirmations about the real world, leaves unexplained the relationship of mathematics to reality.

The formalist school led by David Hilbert proposes that each branch of mathematics be built upon a set of logical and mathematical axioms. The axioms are formulated in terms of symbolic statements to which no meaning is to be attached and the theorems result from the pure manipulation of symbols according to rules contained in the axioms. This pure formal view avoids use of the word *all*, a source of the most disturbing difficulties. Under this approach mathematics proper becomes a series of meaningless structures. The consistency of these structures was to be established by using some clear and unquestionable logical principles in an extra- or metamathematical domain. But the logician Kurt Gödel soon showed, by symbolizing the metamathematical method and arithmetizing the proof of consistency, that any significant branch must, if consistent, be incomplete and so not encompass significant and even intuitively correct statements of mathematics (which remain undecidable). Alternatively if the branch is complete then it is inconsistent. Consistency, then, implies that mathematics cannot be reduced to axioms for these are inadequate to yield all the conclusions that should be established. On the other hand, completeness implies inconsistency, which is intolerable.

The intuitionist school, championed by the Dutch mathematician L. E. J. Brouwer, starts with the fundamental intuition of the natural numbers and all basic ideas and affirmations are grasped by intuition. Logic is relevant only for communication. The paradoxes are a defect of the logic and since the logic is incidental, the occurrence of paradoxes is unimportant. According to the intuitionists the problem of consistency is also a problem of logic and so it is immaterial. Despite the relative unimportance of logical proof the intuitionists do consider to what extent language and its accompanying logic are adequate to represent the ideas guaranteed by the intuition. They found, for example, that the law of excluded middle may not be used when dealing with actual infinite sets. Moreover, any proofs of existence must be constructive, that is, one cannot establish existence by showing that non-existence leads to a contradiction. Thus to prove that an equation has a root because the assumption it does not lead to a contradiction, is non-constructive. Finally we must allow for undecidable propositions. There are sensible questions which have no answers. Since much of mathematics, for example the theory of irrational numbers and concepts of analysis built on it, does not satisfy these criteria, these parts of mathematics are not accepted. Thus the intuitionists reject a great deal of what has been standard, basic mathematics.

There are objections to all three schools of thought and mathematicians working in the foundations of the subject disagree on which view is acceptable. Hence mathematicians have not eliminated the paradoxes in any way satisfactory to all nor have they established consistency. In fact they no longer agree on what constitutes a valid proof, because they no longer agree on what principles of logic are acceptable. The unsatisfactoriness of the present state of affairs is reflected in the joshing about proofs. Rather ironical are the quips: "Logic is the art of going wrong with confidence." "The virtue of a proof is not that it compels belief but that it suggests doubts." "A proof tells us where to concentrate our doubts." "More vigor and less rigor." "We can no longer hope to be logical; the best we can hope for is not to be illogical."

THE CURRENT RELATIONSHIP OF MATHEMATICS TO SCIENCE

The implications of the new understanding of the nature of mathematics bear directly on the relationship of mathematics to science. The first point is that scientists can no longer rely upon the truth of mathematics. Scientists had come to realize before the mathematicians faced up to their difficulties that science offers convenient theories about physical phenomena but does not offer truths of nature. But all scientists until the late nineteenth century accepted the mathematical element in their work as truth. Now that they know that this is not so, scientists must treat mathematics on the same empirical basis as they treat their own theories. Mathematics is one of the sciences and depends on experimental verification.

The inconsistencies in mathematics pose another threat to science in that any logical system which has inconsistencies is strictly nonsensical. Even if the known paradoxes are resolved, until the consistency of mathematics is established, there is the danger that contradictions will appear at any stage in the scientific uses of mathematics.

One would expect that the deficiences in mathematics would seriously disturb both mathematicians and scientists. The effect, however, has been insignificant and the way in which mathematicians and scientists have been working since 1900 is typical of the way humans meet their problems. The mathematicians who have been supplying foundations for their subject during the last one hundred years may be likened to builders who seek to strengthen the foundation of a building resting on insecure ground. Finding the ground a little farther down seemingly firm, they extend the foundation of the building to this hard ground. But when the building finally rests on this ground it begins to crumble. And so the builders dig still deeper to what surely appears to be unyielding earth and extend the foundation still more. But once again they are disappointed and so they continue digging and extending in the hope that they will reach solid rock and that then the building will be firmly anchored. While the builders dig farther and farther down, the tenants of the building continue to occupy it and do their work. After some time the people working on the foundations get so far below ground that they are completely out of sight and the tenants forget that there is any concern at all about the support of the structure or the danger of collapse. The tenants are the mathematicians and scientists who continue to use the conventional mathematics and who are oblivious to the men concerned with shoring up the foundations.

Another consequence of the loss of truth in mathematics is the abandonment of science by most mathematicians. It was the desire to guarantee the physical correctness of the parallel axiom which led to non-Euclidean geometry. But many mathematicians, either ignorant of the history or deliberately distorting the history to suit their purposes, proclaim that an interest in purely intellectual questions led to non-Euclidean geometry and this creation, nevertheless, proved to be useful (in relativity theory). Hence they argue, any question that seems worthy to the mathematician, regardless of current physical significance, should be investigated. Happy to be relieved of a responsibility to science because they need not be informed in this area, they pursue mathematical themes of their own concoction. They still pay lip service to science and promise that their arbitrary creations will be useful 50 or 100 years from now. Others now completely ignore science and defend mathematics solely as a beautiful, exciting and intrinsically interesting activity.

In the United States 80 to 90% of the mathematicians have turned to fields such as abstract algebra, mathematical logic, and topology, to abstractions and generalizations such as functional analysis, to existence proofs in differential equations, and to axiomatizations of various bodies of thought. Relatively few study the more concrete, physically significant problems notably in differential equations and allied fields. In the sixth decade of a century in which mathematics has been far more active than in any other century one notes rather few new applied fields: non-linear differential equations, integral equations, functions of two complex variables, and asymptotic series solutions of differential equations.

The warning that mathematicians are abandoning their obligations to science and even risking the drying-up of their ideas has been sounded by many men. In an article in the American Mathematical Monthly of 1944 the distinguished mathematical physicist J. L. Synge said, "Most mathematicians work with ideas which, by common consent, belong definitely to mathematics. They form a closed guild. The initiate foreswears the things of the world, and generally keeps his oath. Only a few mathematicians roam abroad and seek mathematical sustenance in problems arising directly out of other fields of science. In 1744 or 1844 this second class included almost the whole body of mathematicians. In 1944 it is such a small fraction of the whole that it becomes necessary to remind the majority of the existence of the minority, and to explain its point of view.

"The minority does not wish to be labelled 'physicist' or 'engineer,' for it is following a mathematical tradition extending through more than twenty centuries and including the names Euclid, Archimedes, Newton, Lagrange, Hamilton, Gauss, Poincaré. The minority does not wish to belittle in any way the work of the majority, but it does fear that a mathematics which feeds solely on itself will in time exhaust its interest."

In an essay entitled "The Mathematician" published in 1947 John von Neumann ends with this: "As a mathematical discipline travels far from its empirical source, or still more, if it is a second and third generation only indirectly inspired by ideas coming from 'reality,' it is beset with very grave dangers. It becomes more and more purely aestheticizing, more and more purely *l'art pour l'art*. This need not be bad, if the field is surrounded by correlated subjects, which still have closer empirical connections, or if the discipline is under the influence of men with an exceptionally well developed taste. But there is a grave danger that the subject will develop along the lines of least resistance, that the stream, so far from its source, will separate into a multitude of insignificant branches, and that the discipline will become a disorganized mass of details and complexities. In other words, at a great distance from its empirical source, or after much 'abstract' inbreeding, a mathematical subject is in danger of degeneration."

In his necrology on Franz Rellich in the *Mathematische Annalen* of 1957, Richard Courant affirms that if present trends continue the real (angewandte) mathematics of the future will be created by physicists and engineers and professional mathematicians will have no contact with this development.

THE CURRENT VIEW OF PROOF

The present state of mathematics as a distinct subject is indeed anomalous. Its claim to truth has been abandoned. Its efforts to eliminate the paradoxes and establish the consistency of its reasoning have thus not only failed but also have even produced controversy as to what correct reasoning in mathematics is and as to what the proper foundations of mathematics are. The claim, therefore, to impeccable reasoning must also be abandoned. In view of these unresolved issues what should the *modus vivendi* of mathematics be? Should we conclude that mathematics as a soundly established body of knowledge is an illusion? Should we abandon deductive proof and resort to intuitively sound arguments, to empirical evidence, and to inductive arguments? After all, the physical sciences use such modes of reasoning and, even where they have used deductive mathematics, they have not been concerned with the mathematicians' standard of rigor. This is not the advisable path. Anyone who has some knowledge of the contributions of mathematics would not abandon the ideals and goals of the subject. What is needed is a new evaluation of the nature of mathematics.

First of all, deductive proof does have immense value. Beyond the murky foundations it does permit an effective and reliable organization of knowledge. Moreover, proof gives us relative assurance. We become convinced thereby that some theorem is correct if some reasonably sound and intuitively more acceptable statements about numbers or geometrical figures are correct. Proof thus establishes more doubtful statements on the basis of less doubtful ones and reduces the number of statements we must accept on an intuitive or heuristic basis. The security with which we can use the central body of mathematics increases as we narrow the difficulties to a limited area.

However, we are now compelled to accept the fact that there is no such thing as an absolute proof or a completely rigorous proof. We know that if we question the statements we accept on an intuitive basis, we shall be able to prove these only if we accept others on an intuitive basis. Nor can we probe these ultimate intuitions too far without running into paradoxes or other unresolved difficulties, some lying in the realm of logic itself. Sometime about 1900, the famous French mathematician Jacques Hadamard said, "Logic sanctions the conquests of the intuition." We can no longer accept this judgment. It is more appropriate to say with Herman Weyl, "Logic is the hygiene which the mathematician practices to keep his ideas healthy and strong."

We must recognize that rigor is not an actuality but a goal, a goal to be sought but very likely never to be attained. We should make constant efforts to strengthen what we have without expecting ever to perfect it. Yet the search for additional strength not only yields strength but also produces the very great values which mathematics has furnished in the past. If then we reorient our attitude toward mathematics, we shall be, I believe, more content to pursue the subject despite the fact that we have been disillusioned. This view of mathematics is epitomized in the American mathematician E. H. Moore's statement, "Sufficient unto the day is the rigor thereof."

III. Science and Technology in The Emerging Nations

Abdus Salam

RIGHT FROM THE days of Merlin at the Court of King Arthur, the scientist has enjoyed the dubious repute of a wizard. One of the most famous scientist-wizards of the Middle Ages was Michael, the Scot who was celebrated in verse by his countryman Sir Walter Scott in the "Lay of the Last Minstrel." A traveller to the Paynim countries of the East tells us that:

> "In those far climes it was my lot
> To meet the wondrous Michael Scott;
> A wizard of such dreaded fame,
> That when in Salamanca's cave,
> He lifted his magic wand to wave,
> The bells would ring in Notre Dame!"

We are also told Michael's words could cleave the Eildon hills in three; he could bridle River Tweed with a curb of stone; at a sign from him you could be transported from Portugal to Spain in the space of less than a night.

We do not know if Michael the Scot did really command the powers ascribed to him. Even if he did, he could only have anticipated the men of Alamogordo and Cape Kennedy by just a few centuries. We may, however, with reason inquire why he did acquire in the Middle Ages the dread reputation that haunted his memory.

Michael the Scot was a humble scholar. Born in 1175, he was one of those few inquiring men who wished to pursue science with teachers who were currently creating it. At the age of twenty-five he

ABDUS SALAM, Director of the International Institute of Theoretical Physics in Trieste; Professor of Theoretical Physics, University of London. He is chief scientific advisor to the President of Pakistan. An AFOSR grantee in elementary particle physics.

travelled to the Islamic University of Toledo in Spain; to study he had to learn Arabic, the then language of science. From Toledo he proceeded to Padua and Rome, teaching and translating what he had learned. His was the first translation of Aristotle's *De Anima* into Latin, not from the original Greek which Michael knew not, but from Arabic. His repute for wisdom, for wizardry, was a tribute, if you wish, to Arabic mathematics, Arabic astronomy, Arabic medicine of that day.

I have thus chosen to preface my account of science and technology in the developing world today with an account of Michael the Scot. The history of science, like the history of all civilization, has gone through cycles. Some seven centuries back, at least some of the developing countries of today were in the forefront of scientific endeavour; they were the standard bearers, the pioneers. George Sarton in his monumental five-volume *History of Science* chose to divide his story of achievement in sciences into ages, each age lasting half a century. With each half century he associated one central figure; thus 500 B.C.-450 B.C. Sarton calls the Age of Hippocrates; 450 B.C. to 400 B.C. is the Age of Plato. This is followed by the half centuries of Aristotle, of Euclid, then of Archimedes and so on. From 650 A.D.-700 A.D. is the half century of the last Chinese scientist I-ching. From 750 A.D. in an unbroken succession for 300 years, are the Ages of Jabir, Khwarizmi, Razi, Masudi, Wafa, Biruni and Omar Khayyam—Arabs, Turks, Afghans and Persians—men belonging to the culture of Islam. Around 1100 A.D. appear the first Western names, but the honors are still shared between the East and the West for two hundred years more. From 1350 A.D., however, science was created only in the West. No wonder then that Michael the Scot, in 1200 A.D., had to travel to Toledo to complete his scientific education. No wonder that this association with the infidel earned him an excommunication. No wonder that Dante consigned him to Hell.

I hope I shall not be accused of parochialism in reminding you thus that in the march of science and civilization other cultures, other lands, have played their humble role. This central fact is important to the theme I wish to unfold; it determines a whole set of attitudes, the whole approach of the emerging countries to acquiring modern scientific and technological competence is conditioned by it.

Now, throughout the ages its scientific and technical knowledge have influenced the material prosperity of a civilization. Technical advances in agriculture, in manufacturing methods, in transport have occurred in all human societies and these have always led to increased prosperity. But it is a central fact of human history that something unique occurred with the 18th and 19th century breakthroughs in physics and chemistry and metallurgy, something unique, something massive, something cumulative. The firm and the scientific mastery of natural law acquired in the last two hundred years gave man so much power, and led to such a great increase in production, that for the first time in man's history a purposeful application of scientific and technological techniques can transform the entire material basis of whole societies, eliminating hunger and want, and ceaseless toil and early death for the whole human race. Technical competence and material prosperity have become synonymous and it is this cardinal fact that the poorer two-thirds of humanity is beginning to realize. It is this cardinal fact that the developing world must come to grips with today.

How did this great division of humanity—the division of the rich and the poor, both materially and technologically—first come about? Clearly I have no competence to speak for all developing countries; there is one part of the world, however, I know much better than any other—my own country, Pakistan. Instead of generalities I propose to give you a detailed picture of Pakistan's technological past, its present and its hopes for the future. In many ways the problems I shall deal with are typical of the rest of the developing world. In particular I shall show you how important an impact on modern Pakistan the imported technology of the 19th century had. And I shall endeavour to show how many of its problems arise because we did not adjust to the technology of the 20th century in time.

I shall start my story about three centuries ago. Around 1660 two of the greatest monuments of modern history were erected—one in the West and one in the East; St. Paul's Cathedral in London and the Taj Mahal at Agra in the India of the Great Mughals. Between them these two monuments symbolize, perhaps better than words can describe, the comparative level of craftsmanship, the comparative level of architectural technology, of affluence and sophistication the two cultures had achieved at that epoch of history.

But at about the same time was also created, and this time only in the West, a third monument, a monument still greater in its eventual import for humanity. This was Newton's *Principia* published in 1687. Newton's work had no counterpart in the India of the Mughals. The impulse-springs of Islamic science had dried up earlier. The Taj Mahal was about the last flowering of a tradition, a tradition that was no longer creative, a tradition that was soon to wither and die.

The two cultures, the two technologies, that of the East and the West, came into sharp impact within a hundred years of the building of the Taj. In 1757, to be precise, the superior fire-power of Clive's small arms inflicted, on the battle grounds of Plassey, a humiliating military defeat on the descendants of the great Mughal. Another hundred years passed and in 1857, the last of the Mughals had been forced to relinquish the Imperial Crown of Delhi to Queen Victoria. With him there passed not only an empire, but also a whole tradition in art, in technology and in learning. By 1857, English had supplanted Persian as the language of state; the medical canons of Aricenna had been forgotten and the traditional art of fine muslin-weaving in Dacca had disappeared to give way to the cotton prints of Lancashire.

But from the decay of the Mughal state in 1857, from the embers as it were, there also arose the beginning of a new and modern state—the state of Pakistan in the northwest and east corners of the Indian sub-continent.

West Pakistan, of which I shall principally speak today, is a state twice as large in area and thrice as populous as California. It is a dry, parched land, watered by the mighty Indus and its five tributaries, the Ghelum, Chenab, Ravi, Beas and Sutlej. In 1857, when the British came to it as conquerers, they found ribbons of cultivation a few miles wide on either side of each of the five rivers. Between these cultivated ribbons lay stretches of parched desert.

Not content with these ribbon-like patches of cultivation, some far-sighted men in the Indian Civil Service harnessed the technology of their day to create a garden out of the scrub and the desert. They built low dams across the five rivers on foundations of gravel and sand—structures which had rarely been attempted elsewhere and whose essential stability remains something of a miracle to most hydraulic engineers till this day. Behind the dams they diverted the waters into great new canals. These canals have a total length of

10,000 miles; some of the biggest are as large as the Colorado River. With the canal system was created a fine railway network and perhaps the best road system east of Suez. West Pakistan, as a consequence, multiplied in prosperity, fertility and population. It was in this sense that modern Pakistan—in company with many another ex-colonial country—was a creation of the 19th century technology.

But even after such a heavy initial dose of technology, and again very typically, Pakistan failed to become a technologically advanced country. Something went grievously wrong, for the first flush of prosperity lasted no more than a few decades. The country was built upon just one resource, agriculture, and agricultural production did not keep in step with the population increase. Even on the purely technical side, soon after its inception the very miracle of West Pakistan's canal network began slowly to stifle the fertility it was meant to create by spreading the blight of waterlogging and salinity in areas through which the canals passed.

The reasons for this failure of technology were not difficult to find. The technology which created Pakistan did not touch us more than skin-deep. It was a graft that never took, not something that became an integral part of our lives, and all for one basic reason. The only way to communicate the garnered wisdom and knowledge of one generation of men to another is by precept and education. It may be hard to believe, but in Pakistan no provision whatsoever was made for scientific or technical or vocational education.

Thus, even though the entire object of bringing the canal waters was to increase agricultural production, no one dreamed of introducing agricultural technology in the educational system. Something like thirty-one liberal arts colleges were built in the country, one in every district headquarters, to teach British history, the metaphysics of Aristotle, the laws of equity and the principles of jurisprudence, but the whole of West Pakistan and the whole of East Pakistan had to be content with just one agricultural and just one engineering college—and this for a population then approaching fifty million. I cannot begin to convey my own personal sense of disbelief when some years ago I was told that in the United States every state university grew around the nucleus of an agricultural faculty with every other faculty added later, so contrary this was to anything I had been used to in Pakistan.

The story repeated itself at all levels. The results could have been foreseen. The level of agricultural practice remained as static as under the Mughals. The chemical revolution of fertilizers and pesticides touched us not. The manufacturing crafts went into complete oblivion. Even a steel plow had to be imported from England.

Why did the British administration fail to place any emphasis on technical education, on mechanical skills, or on agricultural husbandry? For mechanical skills there is perhaps a simple explanation. In the economic organization of the empire, Britain was to be the only manufacturing unit. All its other parts—like the American colonies, India, Nigeria, Sudan—were to supply raw materials. Thus, from a British administrator's point of view there was no need to foster mechanical or industrial skills, for these would never be exercised. But by the same token this attitude is harder to understand so far as agriculture is concerned; the attitude which, for example, failed to build up a proper agricultural advisory and extension service.

Perhaps there is a simpler and more charitable explanation possible. The educational system of the British India was essentially the creation of one man, the great historian Lord Macaulay. Writing his recommendations in 1835, he strove to give us the best that Britain could then offer. This best unfortunately did not embrace science and technology. In so far as Britain's industrial revolution had been brought about by gifted amateurs, there was in the Britain of the 19th century no appreciation of the role of technical education in fostering industrial growth. The first Royal Commission on Technical Education did not report until 1884. The first parliamentary grant in Britain for scientific and technical education amounted to no more than three thousand dollars. The first polytechnics did not come until 1890. Unlike Germany, modern Russia, or the United States, Britain did not build up an industrial society through the medium of education. Whether or not Britain suffered at all in the long run I shall not say, but for Pakistan, whose whole educational system was patterned on that of the British, this was disastrous.

In 1947, after ninety years of foreign rule, the nation started on a new phase of life. For us in Pakistan the struggle for independence has been fought on two fronts, one against the British for liberty and the second for recognition of our separate existence. On the debit side, we started with a desperately poor population, with a per capita income of fifteen cents a day. We started with no manufacturing capacity or skills and we started with a primitive agriculture, with one-fifth of our cultivated area bedeviled by the twin curses of salinity and waterlogging.

On the credit side, however, we had two assets. First, the revolution of rising expectations had hit Pakistan as strongly as it hit the rest of the underdeveloped world. Second, although there was no clear notion of how to effect an economic transformation of society, there was no resistance to newer ideas or to a newer organization of life. Like every nation smarting under recent defeat of arms, we too had passed through the phase when everything Western was an anathema, but in 1947 this phase of our history was a long way behind us.

We spent the first ten years of our independent existence in trying to redress almost feverishly, and perhaps with complete disregard of sound economics or personal suffering of the consumer, the imbalance of industrialization. The basic consumer industries—like textiles, sugar, cement and paper manufacture—were hastily created by private enterprise. But it may perhaps be right to date the era of our purposeful growth from 1958, the year that President Ayub Khan came into power and the State Planning Commission started to function with the fullest vigor. About then we began receiving the maximum help from our friends and allies, not the least from the United States, and since then we have saved and invested yearly some twenty per cent of our national income.

For the last three years the economy has grown at the rate of six per cent, the highest in Asia. Industrially we have reached the maturity of being able to project a modest heavy industrial and chemical complex based mainly on the major industrial raw material which we possess in plenty, natural gas. A modern shipbuilding yard now exists in Karachi; three refineries and two steel plants of half-million ton capacity are being erected. Since 1950, four technical universities have functioned and a number of others are projected. As a measure of the level of craftsmanship achieved, Pakistan is at present the largest net external supplier of surgical instruments to the United Kingdom. In agriculture we are on the threshold of the chemical revolution. One of the most imaginative of recent scientific missions was the 1961 team of university scientists, hydrologists, agriculturists, and engineers assembled on President Kennedy's behest by Jerome Wiesner and led by Roger Revelle to study the salinity and waterlogging problem in West Pakistan. Waterlogging and salinity are as old as irrigation itself. It has also been known for long that proper drainage is the only answer, but what makes horizontal drainage impossible in the Indus plain is the unfortunate circumstance that the plain slopes no more than a foot per mile. Horizontal drainage would be prohibitive in cost. The Revelle team suggested vertical drainage instead—mining of fresh water from an underground reservoir known to exist by a network of deep tube-wells. Some of the water would seep back underground, leaching away the salt in the process. Also the general lowering of the water table on account of the pumping would cure waterlogging.

I am dwelling on the work of this team in such detail for there is something important I wish to illustrate—the impact of high-caliber scientific minds on problems relatively old. Vertical drainage had in fact been tried in Pakistan for the last fifteen years. But the results were discouraging. The great contribution of the team was to stress that the difficulty came from using the method on too small a scale. A single well, for example, has no effect on the water-level because water seeps in from the surrounding areas as fast as it is removed. To achieve a substantial lowering of the water table one must exploit the simple fact that with increasing size of a surface, the area increases more rapidly than the perimeter—the same principle which in wartime Britain made the British decide in favor of large transatlantic convoys as affording better protection against submarines' peripheral attacks rather than convoys of tiny size. Revelle's calculations—using extensive digital and linear programming at Harvard—showed that if one dealt with areas no smaller than one million acres (roughly 40 sq. miles) the peripheral seepage would not win against the area pumping; one might then hope to eliminate waterlogging within a year or two. It is two years since Revelle's report was presented. Its results have been brilliantly confirmed in the last year, in a region west of Lahore. An earlier tube-well scheme covering 60,000 acres had no effect on the water level; a larger scheme covering 1.2 million acres has drawn down the water level by about two feet—with an increase of crop yield of 50-75%.

I said earlier I shall deal extensively with Pakistan and the impact of technology and science on its growth for two reasons; firstly because I am personally more familiar with the problems of my own country; secondly because I believe the picture of Pakistan is typical of the bulk of the developing world. Pakistan presents us the picture of an ancient civilization, not too distantly in a scientific and a cultural lead; a proud nation humiliated into military submission in the recent past. The defeat was followed by an introduction of newer technological ideas and the harnessing of its rivers for agricultural growth. The new pattern was beneficial in part, but there was no wholeness to it; there was no fostering of a whole scientific and technological tradition accompanying an importation of technology. No educational system was created to carry the mastery of newer technologies further. After the first flush of prosperity, there was the inevitable over-population, the inevitable hunger and poverty. Exactly the same pattern repeated itself in India, in China, in Indonesia, in Egypt, in North Africa and elsewhere. But what of today? The great colonial convulsions of the last twenty years have freed our nations from tutelage. We can plan and execute our own destinies purposefully, remembering the lessons of the recent past. In varying degrees we have realized that there is only one way forward; to pick up the threads of technological and scientific revolution, to bring back skills and learning from the modern Toledoes. Unfortunately the magnitude of the problems is so great, the scale so vast, that along with skills we also need large quantities of scarce capital. Science and technology are no magic wands; machines cost money to make. A Roger Revelle may make the brilliant diagnosis— area versus perimeter for Pakistan's waterlogging problem—but the tube-wells must be fabricated, not just of iron and brass but sometimes, for the very saline soils, of costly fibreglass.

The path which most developing countries are taking is more or less uniform. First and foremost is the acquiring of basic skills for the operation of a technological economy with priority on the exploitation of natural resources. These may be natural gas or oil, aluminum ores or the good agricultural earth. For the larger countries this may mean building of fertilizer-producing machinery and processing and fabrication plants. There is nothing more sensitively felt in a developing country than the feeling that those in a richer region would like to see it devote itself to primary production and no more. I said earlier the pattern all over the developing world is the same. To substantiate this let me quote to you from the United Nations Special Fund report. This fund operates with a capital of about half a billion dollars and is one of the brightest landmarks of international co-operation initiated by that much maligned organization. Let us follow alphabetically the requests to it of some of the various governments:

Afghanistan: Request for Survey of Ground Water Investigation.
Argentine: Mineral Survey in the Andes.
Bolivia: Mineral Survey of the Altiplano.
Brazil: Survey of the San Francisco River Basin and Rock-Salt Deposits.
Burma: Survey of Lead, Zinc Mining and Smelting.

       *   *   *   *   *

Pakistan: Engineers' Training.

Everywhere it is the same; acquiring of skills, and exploitation of natural resources, more and more productive agriculture.

These are the major, the urgent tasks of science and technology today for the emerging countries. In fulfilling these we need all the help, all the co-operation we can get.

IV. Implications of Population Trends for the Military

Philip M. Hauser

World Population Growth

Although the first complete census of mankind has yet to be taken, it is possible to reconstruct, within reasonable error limits, the estimated population of the world from the end of the Neolithic period (the new Stone Age) in Europe (8000-7000 B.C.). At that time, world population is estimated at some ten million. At the beginning of the Christian Era the population of the world probably numbered between 200 and 300 million. At the beginning of the Modern Era (1650) world population reached about 500 million. In 1965 world population totaled 3.3 billion. A relatively simple analysis of these numbers discloses that an enormous increase in the rate of world population growth has occurred, especially during the past three centuries.

It is estimated that for the some six hundred thousand years of the Paleolithic Age (the old Stone Age) population growth perhaps approximated 0.02 per thousand per year. During the three centuries of the Modern Era population growth increased from about three per thousand to ten per thousand per year during the interwar years. The rate of world population growth continued to accelerate after World War II, so that in 1965 it approximated 20 per thousand per year. In the course of man's inhabitation of this globe, then, his rate of population growth has increased from a rate of about two per cent per millennium to two per cent per year, a thousandfold increase in growth rate.

PHILIP M. HAUSER, Professor and Chairman of the Department of Sociology, The University of Chicago. Dr. Hauser was chairman of the technical advisory committee for the 1960 Population Census, and is a former acting director of the Bureau of the Census. He is currently director of the University of Chicago's Population Research and Training Center.

Although two per cent per year may seem like a small return on investment to persons fortunate enough to have funds out at interest, it turns out to be a truly astonishing rate of world population growth. For example, to produce the present population of the world, about 3 billion, one dozen persons increasing at a rate of two per cent per year would have required only 976 years. Yet *homo sapiens* alone have been on this earth at least 25 to 30 thousand years. Similarly the same one dozen persons reproducing at the rate of two per cent per year since the beginning of the Christian Era could have by 1965 had over 300 million descendants for each one actually present on the face of the earth.

Further appreciation of the meaning of a two per cent rate of increase per year is gained by observing the population that this growth rate would produce in the future. It would from the present population of over 3 billion provide enough people, in lock step, to reach from the earth to the sun in 237 years. It would give one person for each square foot of land surface on the globe, including mountains, deserts and the arctic wastes, in about six and one-half centuries. It would generate a population which would weigh as much as the earth itself in 1,566 years. These periods of time may seem long when measured by the length of the individual life time. But they are but small intervals of time measured in the time perspective of the evolutionary development of man.

Projections of this type, of course, are not to be interpreted as predictions. They merely help to indicate the meaning of the present rate of growth. They also permit another firm conclusion, namely: that the present rate of world population growth cannot possibly persist for very long into the future. As a matter of fact, in the long run, given a finite globe and excluding the possibilities of exporting human population to outer space, any rate of population growth would in time saturate the globe and exhaust space itself. In the long run, man will necessarily be faced with the problem of restricting his rate of increase to maintain some balance between his numbers and the finite dimensions of this planet.

It took most of the millennia of man's habitation of this planet to produce a population as great as one billion persons simultaneously alive. This population was not achieved until approximately 1825. To produce a population of two billion persons simultaneously alive required only an additional 105 years—for this number was achieved by 1930. To reach a population of 3 billion persons required only an additional 30 years—for this was the total in 1960. Continuation of the trend would produce a fourth billion by 1977, in only 17 years; a fifth billion by 1987, in only ten years; and a sixth billion in 1996, in only 8 years.

Analyses of this type have led the student of population, the demographer, to use emotional and unscientific language on occasion to describe population developments. Such a phrase as "the population explosion" is admittedly non-scientific language; but it serves to emphasize the dramatic increase in man's rate of growth and to call attention to its many implications.

EXPLANATION OF EXPLOSION

Why has the rate of world population growth increased so greatly? Although some changes in birth rates were also involved, it is clear that the major element in the great acceleration of population growth first evident in Europe and areas of European settlement, was the decline in the death rate. Three factors contributed to this decline. The first was the general increase in level of living resulting from technological advances and increased productivity and the achievement of long periods of peace and tranquility by reason of the emergence of relatively powerful and stable central government. The second major factor accounting for the decrease in mortality was the achievement of environmental sanitation and improved personal hygiene. During the 19th century great strides were made in purifying food and water and improving personal cleanliness, which contributed materially to the elimination of parasitic, infectious, and contagious diseases. The third major factor is, of course, to be found in the great and growing contribution of modern medicine—enhanced by the recent progress in chemotherapy and the insecticides.

These developments during the Modern Era upset the equilibrium between the birth rate and the death rate that characterized most of the millennia of human existence. In 18th century France, for example, of a thousand infants born, 233 had died before they reached age 1; 498 had died before they reached age 20; and 786 had died before they reached age 60. In contrast, in present-day France, of a thousand infants born, only 40 had died before age 1; only 60 had died before age 20; and only 246 had died before age 60. In 18th century France, of the original one thousand infants only 214 survived to age 60. In contemporary France, 754 of the original infants were still alive at age 60. As a result of such decrease in death rates, the one hundred million Europeans of 1650 had three centuries later about 940 million descendants.

Prior to World War II, the spectacular decrease in the death rate of the economically advanced nations had not been shared by most of the population of the world. Of the people of non-European stock, only Japan had managed appreciably to increase longevity. The two-thirds of the world's people who live in the economically under-developed nations—Asia, Latin America, and Africa—before World War II had achieved some decrease in mortality, largely through contact with advanced nations. But most of the world's people prior to World War II were characterized by an expectation of life at birth no greater than that which Western Europeans experienced during the Middle Ages.

This situation has dramatically changed since the end of World War II. A combination of factors including the advent of the United Nations and the specialized agencies with programs emphasizing economic development and dissemination of chemotherapy and in-secticides have opened up to the mass of the world's people the achievement of 20th century death rates. Since the end of World War II, the decline in mortality among the economically under-developed areas of the world have been more dramatic than that which was experienced in the industralized areas.

Longevity is now increasing much more rapidly in the less developed areas than it did among Europeans and European stock because of the much more powerful means now available for eliminating causes of mortality. For example, the death rate of the Moslem population in Algeria in 1946-47 was higher than that of Sweden in 1771-80, more than a century and a half earlier. By 1955, however, in eight years, the decrease in the death rate in Algeria was greater than that Sweden experienced during the century from 1775 to 1875. Between 1940 and 1960, Mexico, Costa Rica, Venezuela, Ceylon, Malaya, and Singapore were among the nations which decreased their death rates by more than 50 per cent. Ceylon's death rate was decreased by more than 50 per cent in less than a decade.

While death rates fell sharply in the underdeveloped areas, birth rates remained at high levels. Whereas birth rates in the economically advanced areas were mainly between 17 to 23 (per 1000 persons per year), those of the developing regions were predominantly above 40. As a result, whereas growth rates in the history of the industrialized nations rarely exceeded 1 per cent per annum without immigration, annual growth rates in the developing nations are above 2 per cent, and many are above 3 per cent. A 3 per cent per annum growth rate doubles a population in 23 years. Since the developing nations contain over two thirds of the world's population, the growth rate of the world as a whole is accelerating despite the fertility decline which began during the 19th century in the economically advanced nations. Among the non-Western nations of appreciable size, only in Japan has the birth rate declined. The developing nations in Asia, Latin America, and Africa, with their 20th century death rates and medieval birth rates, are not only perpetuating but also are actually accelerating the world population explosion.

WORLD PROJECTIONS TO 2000

The United Nations has issued provisional population projections for the world and for the developed and developing areas, to the end of the century. They indicate that if present trends were to continue, world population would reach 7.4 billion by 2000.

If the birth rate were to decline, at varying rates and with different timing, while mortality continues its decline, three additional projections are calculated by the United Nations and published as "high, low, and medium variant projections." The "high" variant gives a world population in 2000 of 6.8 billion, the "medium" variant 6.0 billion, and the "low" variant 5.3 billion. On the basis of its analysis, the United Nations publication concludes that "it is safe to estimate that the world's population in the year 2000 will be no more than 6,500 and no less than 5,600 million provided unforeseeable events having large consequences in a major portion of the world do not occur."

Each of the United Nations variants below the projection based on the continuation of present trends assumes a reduction of birth rates during the remainder of this century in present high fertility areas. It must be emphasized that up to this time there is no firm evidence, despite specific efforts, that such reductions in the birth rate have yet occurred among the mass illiterate and impoverished populations of Asia, Latin America, and Africa. In consequence, the projection based on the continuation of present trends cannot be dismissed as outside the range of possibility. Any of the other variant projections, then, have built into them assumptions of fertility decline that at the present may be more accurately described as wishful thinking than realistic. For purposes of this discussion the United Nations "high" variant projection will be employed, therefore, even though the United Nations accepts its "median" variant as the most probable. It should be stressed, however, that the discussion which follows and the conclusions reached would not vary significantly if the "medium" or, for that matter any of the other projections were used.

On the basis of the "high" projection, the population of the world as a whole would increase from about three billion in 1960 to 6.8 billion by the year 2000. Hence, world population would more than double during the remainder of this century. The effect of declining mortality especially in the less developed areas, may be readily seen by comparing anticipated growth in the second half of this century with actual growth during the first half. Between 1900 and 1950, world population increased by less than one billion persons. Between 1950 and 2000, the "high" projection indicates an increase of 4.3 billion persons. That is, the absolute increase in the population of the world during the second half of this century may be almost four and one-third times as great as that during the first half of the century. During the second half of this century, there could be a greater increase in world population than was achieved in all the millennia of human existence up to the present time.

Extension of the "high" variant projection, according to the United Nations, produces a world population of 14 billion by 2050. Thus, it is possible that children now entering school will, during their lifetimes, be living in a world with almost five times its present numbers.

PROJECTIONS OF DEVELOPED AND LESS DEVELOPED AREAS

Of special economic and political import for the remainder of this century is the differential in the growth rate of the "developed" and the "developing" areas, respectively. The United Nations "high" projections indicate that the less developed areas would have an aggregate population of about 5.5 billion persons by 2000, whereas the more developed areas would total about 1.4 billion. According to these projections, then, the less developed areas with a population of 2.2 billion in 1960 would increase by some 3.3 billion persons by the end of the century, or by 150 per cent. In contrast, the more developed areas would increase by only 523 million persons, or by about 60 per cent. The population increase in the less developed areas would be over 6 times as great as that in the more developed areas. Moreover, it may be noted that the less developed areas, according to this projection—a quite plausible one—would increase in the last four decades of this century by a greater number of persons than the total present population of the globe.

In 1960, about 71 per cent of the world population lived in the less developed areas and only 29 per cent in the more developed. By 2000, it is possible that the population in the less developed areas would have increased to 80 per cent of the world's total, and that the population in the present more developed areas would have shrunk to 20 per cent.

The significance of present and prospective rates of population growth is to be found in their implications for levels of living and world politics.

WORLD RESOURCES

Let us examine first of all the often discussed relation of population growth to resources and especially to food supply. A recent analysis of the world resources picture by Joseph L. Fisher and Neal Potter of Resources for the Future, Inc. indicates that there is neither justification for the belief that the world is faced with an imminent exhaustion of critical materials or the belief that man's ingenuity can resolve all the problems that may be precipitated by the increasing pressure of population upon resources. The picture in respect of raw materials is quite mixed. The world outlook, and that for the developing areas in general, is rather good in respect of energy commodities and, especially, with the potential of the energy of the atom. But the prospect is less favorable for food and in the past several years has turned dismal.

Almost a doubling of world food output is needed to supply a nutritionally adequate diet to the present populations in the less developed areas. If an adequate diet is to be achieved for a world population which will more than double by 2000, food production must more than quadruple by the end of the century. This would require greater annual increases in food production than have ever been attained over a prolonged period of time. Moreover, within the past few years, population growth has actually outdistanced food production in many areas. A study completed by Lester R. Brown of the U.S. Department of Agriculture in 1965, indicates that in Asia food per person has declined by 4 per cent since 1961, and in Latin America by 6 per cent. In Africa food production has thus far kept up with the population increase but a decline in per capita food production seems imminent. The increase in food production which followed World War II, during which food production greatly declined, leveled off in around 1960, and since then it has failed to keep pace with population growth. The prospect of food shortages in Asia, parts of Latin America and Africa within the next decade or so cannot be easily dismissed.

Critical problems face the world during the remainder of this century, however, even if the threats of lower levels of living or mass starvation fail to materialize. That is, even if present levels of living are maintained to the end of the century in the less developed areas, the world may be plagued by crises that will grow ever more acute and threaten world peace by reasons of continued explosive population growth. This is likely because crucial problems may be propagated by failure to achieve substantially higher levels of living consonant with the new expectations of the mass populations of the world, and the national aspirations of the new, emergent post-war nations.

INTERPLAY OF POPULATION AND OTHER FACTORS

The role of population in determining the world's economic and political destinies during the remainder of this century may be grasped by considering simultaneously the following nine propositions:

1. We live in a world of "have" and "have-not" nations.
2. The international differences in levels of living, by reason of the "revolution of rising expectations," have become "felt" differences.
3. The have-not nations are striving to achieve higher living levels and they have made this goal, apart from independence if they have not yet achieved it, their major national aspiration.
4. There is an inverse correlation between levels of living and present or projected rates of population growth.
5. Rapid population growth is obstructing efforts to raise levels of living in the developing regions of the world.

6. Despite national and international efforts to raise levels of living, disparities between have and have-not nations are increasing rather than decreasing.
7. The accelerating rate of urbanization in the developing areas is exacerbating social unrest, political instability, and threats to world peace.
8. The bi-polar world political alignment—the confrontation between "Capitalist" and "Communist" nations or the "East-West" cold war—is augmenting the tensions arising from frustrations in efforts to raise levels of living in the developing regions.
9. The bi-polar political world is being fragmented by have and have-not differentiation within the Communist bloc and the DeGaullist schism in the Western front. Possible world political realignment is under way on a have, have-not basis rather than on a capitalist-communist basis. This would produce a "North-South" rather than "East-West" confrontation.

Let us proceed to an elaboration of each of these propositions and a consideration of their interrelationships.

HAVE AND HAVE-NOT NATIONS

In 1962 per capita product by continents ranged from $124 per year in Asia and $128 per year in Africa to $2,866 per year in Northern America (America north of the Rio Grande). Asia with 56 per cent of the world's population had but 14 per cent of the world's gross national product. In contrast, Northern America together with Northern and Western Europe and Central Europe excluding the Sino-Soviet Countries, with less than 12 per cent of the world's population, had 59 per cent of the world's gross national product.

Per capita product in 1962 averaged $489 for the world as a whole. The continental sub-regions with per capita product above the world average, one measure of "more developed" areas had an average per capita product of $1,504. In contrast, the continental regions with per capita products below the world average, the "less developed" areas, had a per capita product per year of but $153.

Although questions can be raised about the precision of the estimates of per capita product, nonetheless it is clear that, by and large, there are great disparities among the nations in levels of living.

THE REVOLUTION OF RISING EXPECTATIONS

Throughout human history there have been important differences in levels of living both among and within nations. This fact, however, has gained a new significance in recent times and particularly since the end of World War II. The world has been swept by the "revolution of rising expectations," to use the felicitous phrase of our Assistant Secretary of State, Harlan Cleveland. No longer are there any peoples on the face of the earth who are willing to settle for second place and who are not insisting upon independence if they have not already achieved it.

In consequence, differences between have and have-not nations have in our own time become "felt" differences, a term used some time ago by Warren S. Thompson in his discussion of population problems and world tensions.

ECONOMIC DEVELOPMENT PROGRAMS

The have-not nations of the world are striving to achieve higher living levels. They have made economic development a major national aspiration. The economic development of the underdeveloped areas has indeed become an international goal as set forth in the charter of the United Nations and as manifest in the foreign aid programs of many of the economically advanced nations, both governmental and private. It is probably correct to say that there never was a time in the history of man when the achievement of higher living levels was as universal a goal among all of mankind.

INVERSE RELATION BETWEEN POPULATION GROWTH AND LEVELS OF LIVING

There is an inverse correlation between present and projected rates of population growth and the level of living. For example, of the 8 continental sub-regions which had growth rates above the average for the world as projected from 1962 to 2000, in 7, per capita product was below the average of the world. Contrariwise, in every one of the continental regions in which per capita product is above the world average the annual population growth rate projected between 1962 and 2000 is below that of the world average.

In general, for the world as a whole, poverty is associated with relatively high rates of population increase. Among poor European nations, however, despite their poverty, relatively low population growth rates obtain. But poverty in Europe is a relative matter. It is significant that per capita product in the poor countries of Europe is about 4 to 5 times that of poor countries in Asia, and almost twice that of the poor countries in South and Middle America.

RAPID POPULATION GROWTH OBSTRUCTS ECONOMIC DEVELOPMENT

Study of the relationship between population growth and composition and economic development in recent years has disclosed that population factors operate to obstruct efforts to achieve higher levels of living. Per capita product cannot be increased unless aggregate output rises more rapidly than does population. Rapid population growth obstructs increases in per capita product in a number of ways:

a. it imposes requirements for capital investment which strains the underdeveloped economy even to maintain its current per capita product, let alone to achieve an increase;

b. it produces or threatens to effect population-resources ratios resulting in diminishing returns;

c. it produces an unfavorable age structure, that is, a population with a relatively high proportion of dependents and a relatively low proportion of producers which, all other things being equal, tends to depress product per capita;

d. it requires a relatively large allocation of limited savings to the rearing of the young at the expense of restricting resources available for direct production investment such as investment in fertilizer, tractors, electric power or industrial plant;

e. it diminishes savings available per capita for investment in human resources, that is, investment in education and training.

GAP BETWEEN HAVE AND HAVE-NOT NATIONS IS INCREASING

Despite multilateral and bilateral efforts to assist the developing nations to achieve higher levels of living, such evidence as is available indicates that the disparities between have and have-not nations is increasing rather than decreasing. Have-not nations, relative to have nations, are doubly handicapped in efforts to reduce the disparity in levels of living. First, by reason of their small productive and technological base, even relatively large percentage rates of growth produce rather small absolute increments in levels of living. In contrast the increments attained by the advanced nations are relatively large, even with low rates of economic growth. For example, a ten per cent increase in product in Asia produces an absolute an-

nual increment of about $12 per capita; in northern America a ten
per cent increase produces an increment of $278 per capita.

Second, the rapid rate of population growth in the developing
areas requires more rapid rates of economic growth than in the developed areas merely to maintain already existing levels of living.
Northern America, for example, during the remainder of this century can maintain its present level of living by an economic growth
of 1.6 per cent per annum. Asia, in contrast, to maintain even her
present level of living must achieve an economic growth rate of 2.1
per cent per annum.

THE IMPACT OF URBANIZATION

The rate of world urbanization has been accelerating over the entire period that we are able to measure it with reasonable accuracy,
that is, since 1800. In the 19th century the major impetus to world
urbanization was given by the urbanization in Europe and North
America. During the 20th century, however, the major impetus to
world urbanization is given by rapid urbanization in the developing
regions of Asia, Latin America and Africa.

Rapid urbanization in the developing areas has a special significance in any effort to evaluate factors associated with mounting
world tensions. For poverty and frustration concentrated in the urban setting have a potential for generating social unrest, political
instability and threats to world peace of a much greater magnitude
than poverty and frustration dispersed widely over the countryside.

BI-POLAR POLITICAL WORLD

Since the end of World War II the world has been increasingly
divided into a Capitalist Bloc, a Communist Bloc, and a third neutral or uncommitted bloc. Interestingly enough, one-third of the
world's population is to be found in each of these blocs. Never before in the history of man have such gigantic antagonists as those
represented by the Capitalist and Communist, or "Western" and
"Eastern" blocs been manifest. They confront one another on ideological, economic, social, political, and, from time to time, military
fronts. The East and West, respectively, have each been trying to
win the allegiance of the neutral or uncommitted blocs of nations.
This is manifest in the prolonged struggle for the minds and allegiance of the peoples of South and Southeast Asia. More recently, it

has given rise to increasingly intense competition in Africa; and it continues to constitute a threat to Latin America's identification with the West, especially since the advent of Castro's Cuba. The weapons employed in this confrontation are varied including propaganda, economic aid, subversion, and military confrontation.

The outcome of the cold war, in large measure, may depend on the ability of the developing nations to control their rates of population growth and, thereby, to effect higher levels of living as measured by per capita product. It is almost certain that failure to advance their levels of living would leave the have-not nations of the world more open to the blandishments of the Communist world. The Communist Bloc is in the advantageous position of appealing to anti-imperialist sentiment as it blames Western imperialism for the present poverty of the underdeveloped nations; and of being able thus far, more successfully to exploit the inequities and iniquities characterizing economic and social organization in many of the less developed nations. Moreover, the communist appeal is apparently more alluring and appealing to many peoples than appeals yet developed by the West. The communist appeal in terms of agrarian reform, racial equality, and fuller stomachs seems on the whole to be more effective than the more abstract Western appeal for freedom and democracy.

To the extent, then, that population is a major factor in obstructing economic development, it is a factor which, in the contemporary world, is contributing to mounting social unrest, political instability and threats to world peace which are being exacerbated by the Cold War.

NORTH-SOUTH ALIGNMENT

Over recent years, a schism has become manifest both within the East and West producing tensions within, as well as between, these blocs. Within the East at least, the split between the USSR and China may well have occurred not only from publicized ideological differences, but, also, from their disparity in economic development—from the relative "have" and "have-not" positions of the USSR and China, respectively.

The annual per capita product in 1962 for all the Sino-Soviet countries combined was $269. Within the Sino-Soviet bloc, however, per capita product ranged from $94 in Southeast Asia to an estimated $790 in the USSR. The countries of East Asia in the Communist Bloc, predominantly China, had a per capita product estimated at $95 per annum. The present reluctance of the USSR to use war an an instrument of policy for the expansion of world communism, in contrast with the willingness of China to do so, may well be attributed in some part to the "have" position which Russia has achieved in contrast with China's relatively desperate "have-not" situation. China with a population approximating seven hundred millions and a growth rate approximating perhaps 2 per cent per year may be growing increasingly conscious of the disparities in the man-land ratios in China and in Russian Siberia. In China, inability to control population growth, even though there is much evidence that she is attempting such control, could well constitute a severe threat not only to her neighbors to the south, but also to her Communist neighbors to the north.

This split within the Communist Bloc may conceivably contribute to increased tensions between the "have" and "have-not" nations throughout the world. Certainly China, in attempting to form her own bloc, is finding allies primarily among the poorest nations. It is not impossible that the USSR will find she has more in common with the "have" than with the "have-not" nations, especially if she is successful in her efforts to advance consumption levels. This possibility may be enhanced and accelerated by her fear of China's acquiring atomic weapons.

Thus, it may be that in the coming decades world tensions may revolve around a "North-South" rather than "East-West" axis. The chief threat to peace may be in the level of living disparities between have and have-not nations rather than in differences between capitalist and communist ideologies and systems.

Economic development has as its objective the raising of the level of living of a people. The population of a nation, however, not only reaps the gains of economic development through increased per capita income, but as the human resource, also plays a vital role in its achievement. In the contemporary situation, four aspects of population in the less developed areas are operating to retard economic development. These are the relatively high rate of population growth, unfavorable age structure, unbalanced population distribution, and inadequately educated and trained manpower. All of these obstructions to economic development are amenable to control.

Economic development policies and programs must take into account the role of population factors, in general, and specifically the four aspects of population which have been indicated above. To eliminate the adverse effects of population factors on economic development it is necessary to dampen rates of total population increase, to effect a more favorable age structure, to achieve a more balanced urban-rural population distribution, and to raise the quality of the population by attaining higher levels of education and training. Each of these goals is attainable, and, significantly enough, all may be achieved by the same means—namely, through a decrease in the birth rate. In the contemporary world situation, given the great declines in mortality achieved and in prospect, a decrease in the birth rate would simultaneously reduce rates of population increase, favorably alter the age structure, help to effect better balance between urban and rural population distribution, and permit more adequate and effective investment in human resources.

The two major world ideologies, namely Roman Catholicism and Socialism-Communism, which have been slow to recognize this need and which have resisted efforts to control fertility have perceptibly modified their stand within the past few years.

Although Pope Pius XII recognized the need to control population growth in 1951, it was not until after the general effort to update the Roman Catholic Church's position in the modern world by the late Pope John XXIII and the incumbent Pope Paul VI that recognition of the need for "responsible parenthood" seems to have gained ascendancy over the pro-natalist elements within the Church.

The Communist nations, on the basis of their interpretation of Karl Marx, until relatively recently, also opposed population control. The Communist world has considered birth control, or "neo-Malthusianism," as an instrument by means of which "imperialist capitalist powers" attempt "to subdue and exploit" the "have-not" peoples. But Mainland China, in 1953, after her Census disclosed there were 100 million more Chinese (583 million) than had been previously estimated, was quick to attempt to slow down her rate of population increase; and the Soviet Union and other Communist nations have reversed the position they took at the World Population Conference in Rome in 1954. The Soviet Union is no longer opposed to fertility control. It, however, does believe that it will come about automatically as a consequence of industrialization and urbanization and, therefore, need not be actively promoted.

IMPLICATIONS FOR NATIONAL DEFENSE

The materials presented above indicate that explosive population growth may be a factor in heating up the cold war and in determining whether peace or war will be the lot of the world during the remainder of this century. But population numbers, in my judgment, will not be a major factor in determining the outcome of a major war. To be sure a major war can be fought only by nations of some appreciable size. Apart from this consideration, however, manpower alone will not determine military strength. Other ingredients may prove to be more important than manpower in successful defense or offense. Among the ingredients will be such factors as technology, including military technology; and population quality, that is education and skill, incentive and motivation, and national unity and solidarity. It is not possible to discuss these factors within the scope of this paper but they must not be ignored in considering factors in military power.

In conclusion, then, it should be emphasized that world population trends constitute a major threat to peace during the remainder of this century. Any effort to evaluate the demands that may be placed on the U.S. military forces during the next few decades must, therefore, take into consideration the factors outlined above; and they should also include analysis of domestic population trends and prospects—another subject beyond the scope of this paper.

V. The Frontiers of Psychology

Ernest R. Hilgard

MANY PSYCHOLOGISTS work in the spirit of pure or basic science, seeking to establish lawful relationships among phenomena regardless of where these findings may take us. It is not strictly true that the basic scientist is disinterested in the applications of what he finds out, and I wish to digress just a little on my conception of the relationship between basic and applied science.

Over the past several years there has been a growing cry for more investment in basic research relative to the amounts spent on technological developments. While I am, of course, in favor of pure science and basic research, care has to be taken that this emphasis may not be distorted in the other direction. I sometimes refer to the cult of pure science, which places such a high value on pure science that the more remote, esoteric, and sometimes trivial an investigation becomes, the more it shows that those who support it have the right attitude toward science. I have found this in agencies responsible for distributing categorical money, that is, money intended for a specific purpose: the more peripheral the project to this central intent, the more favorable its reception, because then the grantors are showing that they are interested in basic research. This may be something of a caricature, but I believe the warning is worth sounding. If we place all the prestige on the side of basic science and relegate developmental and applied work to the less imaginative and less competent, we will make just as great mistakes as if we starve pure science. There is a division of labor involved, and a balanced attitude, with mutual respect, is what we need. The history of science would bear me out in this. Very often practical technology has run ahead of pure science and contributed instruments that in turn

ERNEST R. HILGARD is Professor of Psychology at Stanford University, where he has been a member of the faculty since 1933. Dr. Hilgard is a past president of the American Psychological Association. He is the author of the general text INTRODUCTION TO PSYCHOLOGY, *now in its third edition, and of the research volume* HYPNOTIC SUSCEPTIBILITY. *He is an AFOSR grantee.*

advanced pure science. It is only in the very last stages of scientific development that basic science calls the shots. It is worth reminding ourselves that even some of the marvelous developments of the space age, such as guiding space vehicles to the moon, have depended far more on technological developments than on the frontier developments in basic science. I am told that very little beyond Newtonian physics is involved. By contrast, atomic weapons do depend on the basic science developments of modern atomic physics. In any case, there is a constant interchange. The technological developments in the communication industry, to serve telephones, radios, and TV sets, have enormously expanded the instruments available for basic research in physiology and in physiological psychology. What we want is good science, and good science can be done at either the basic or the applied level.

There are some ethical issues involved in applied science that are different from those of pure or basic science. This follows because of the fact that technology is practical and permits control over things and people. In psychology these issues often become quite important. How much are test scores invasions of privacy? Should a child's IQ be recorded at school and not divulged to parents? Should the psychologist help the advertiser to sell goods that the buyer would be better off without? How much should the counselor impose his own moral standards upon his clients or patients? Should the psychologist lend his knowledge to support political candidates?

There was a debate a few years ago between Carl Rogers and B. F. Skinner over the amount of control that a psychologist should propose exercising over people. Rogers took the position that we had better encourage people to lead their own lives and think for themselves; Skinner contended that we inevitably shape them anyhow, so we had better know what we want people to be like and then use our technology to that end (Rogers and Skinner, 1956). The issues are felt keenly enough that a group of psychologists favor what they call a humanistic psychology and publish a *Journal of Humanistic Psychology*. They sometimes refer to their position as a third movement in psychology, the first being behaviorism, the second psychoanalysis. From their vantage point both behaviorism and psychoanalysis are too deterministic and controlling, and they wish a psychology that recognizes human aspirations and latent human potential. While the conception of man is involved in any general psychology, these ethical issues arise chiefly when people are being influenced through psychological technologies, counseling, psychotherapy and education, persuasive techniques of various kinds. We shall see how some of these stirrings are influencing contemporary psychology, even among those who have little sympathy with this "third movement" group.

PSYCHOLOGY AS A BASIC SCIENCE

In order not to spread what I have to say unduly thin, I propose to consider three large topical orientations in basic psychology, and to give limited specimens of current work within each of them. The first of these I shall call *biological psychology*, the second *general experimental psychology,* and the third *social psychology*.

BIOLOGICAL PSYCHOLOGY

Man is undeniably a mammal, and as such shares a mammalian ancestry with other subhuman species. When the psychologist thinks of himself as essentially a biologist, with the evolutionary theory strongly influential as background, his comparative studies of subhuman animals and infants are done in the spirit of other biologists working on problems of genetics or comparative anatomy or embryology, except that he distinguishes his work from theirs by his primary emphasis upon behavior.

The modern science of genetics is, of course, closely related to evolution, in that gene pools and their drift determine evolutionary changes; what is new in emphasis is that many ecological factors influence these shifts, and some of them can be understood better through the history of behavior than through morphology. For example, there are some varieties of moths and grasshoppers which have been classified together morphologically, but they are now assigned to different species because of differences in their behavior (Mayr, 1958). In this case behavior substitutes for morphology as a descriptive character.

It is possible to conduct selective breeding experiments solely on the basis of behavior, and then to find out whether or not the behavior is genetically controlled. For example, some fruitflies (drosophila) make more approach reactions to light than others. If they are sorted out on the basis of approach and non-approach tendencies and mated accordingly, their offspring gradually separate into nearly non-overlapping groups so far as these phototropic tendencies are concerned (Hirsch and Boudreau, 1958).

Another aspect of biological psychology is individual development, the processes of maturing continuing into later life some of the orderly processes found in embryological development. The questions of development are similar to those of genetics. In genetics we ask, "What behavior is inherited and what is acquired?" In development we ask, "What behavior is to be attributed to maturation characteristics of the species, and what is the result of early environmental influences?"

I wish to cite briefly a series of experiments showing how careful we have to be in assigning plausible reasons for the things that occur in experiments, before the necessary controls have been run. For a number of years we have been convinced that the early years are very important in the forming of personality. This we continue to believe. But we thought it especially important that the early years be full of warmth from the parents, and free of anxiety. This still seems like a good idea. What is disquieting is that we thought we had supporting evidence from the animal world. For example, baby rats that were handled and tamed early in life were able to face strangeness and other difficult situations much better than non-handled or neglected ones. But it turns out now that if young rats are taken out of their cages and given electric shocks every day, instead of being fondled, they do just as well as the handled ones when they become adult. This Spartan treatment is better than neglecting them, and perhaps this is the lesson to be learned. According to Levine (1962) who did these studies: "In all respects, in fact, the manipulated infants exhibit a more rapid rate of development. They open their eyes earlier and achieve motor coordination sooner. Their body hair grows faster, and they tend to be significantly heavier at weaning. They continue to gain weight more rapidly than the non-stimulated animals even after the course of stimulation has been completed at three weeks of age. The mechanisms involved are doubtless concerned with the endocrines, which influence responses to stress and have to do with growth processes."

On the suspicion that these results might apply to man also, a Harvard anthropologist (Whiting) and a psychologist now at Stanford (Landauer) felt that it would be interesting to find out what rough handling did to human infants (Landauer and Whiting, 1964).

Of course, they did not set out to find human twin pairs, one member of which would be neglected and the other shocked, but they did the best they could by going to the cross-cultural files and finding cultures that were contrasted in the ways in which they handled infants. They chose male children only, and defined as stressful reactions in infancy such things as piercing and molding, because these are somewhat enduring and must produce some discomfort while they persist. The piercings varied somewhat from one nonliterate culture to another, but included piercing the nose, lips, or ears to receive an ornament; circumcision, innoculation, scarification, or cauterization. Molding included stretching the arms or legs, or shaping the head to conform to an appearance thought desirable within that culture. On the assumption that the infant boys started out even, the hypothesis was that if the rat studies were true the mutilated boys should grow more rapidly and hence should be taller at maturity. They found that those boys mutilated in infancy grew to be some 2.5 inches taller in manhood than those not so mutilated. Let us not jump to conclusions that we should maul our children; apparently in our society we already do enough of it with hospital births, instrumental deliveries, immunization by hypodermic needle, and circumcision; in any case our children are growing taller each generation.

GENERAL EXPERIMENTAL PSYCHOLOGY

I am using this somewhat awkward designation to refer to the kind of psychology which attempts to get at some of the more general laws of behavior in the same sense that general physiology tries to get at the most basic functions of the activity of cells or organ systems. So general experimental psychology tries to get at the basis of perception, of learning, of memory, of problem solving, somewhat independent of the particular content of those perceptions, memories or problems, and even somewhat independent of the particular organism. Such a general science is likely to be a science of models, of simulation, of hypothetical-deductive theories, although there is a great room for differences in approach. One extreme position, which has many adherents, gives itself the somewhat arrogant name of "the experimental analysis of behavior." It is associated with B. F. Skinner, a Harvard psychologist. The main point for Skinner and his followers is that, if appropriately studied, behavior will reveal its own lawfulness, without hypothetical models on the one hand, or explanations in terms of physiology on the other. Many psychologists prefer a reductive model, in which the ultimate explanation of psychological events resides in the nervous system.

The field of general experimental psychology is much too large to treat as a whole, so let me plunge in at one point and talk about the use of computers in simulating psychological events. This will illustrate my point that the model that is used need not be substantive in any ordinary sense, for a computer, while it is composed of a lot of hardware, is essentially some sort of logical machine, and it is the program for the computer that is important, not how the computer is constructed.

The computer is a scientific ally in almost all we do. We have to distinguish, however, between its use as simply a more efficient desk calculator and its use for other purposes. As a calculator, the computer uses an algorithm, and by following specific instructions comes out with the answer. An algorithm is simply a fixed procedure of the kind we learned when we were taught long division or how to extract the square root of a number. Much more interesting are heuristic computers, in which the computer simulates the human problem-solver in trying to find a shortcut, trying to find some approximation to the right answer, or in other ways avoiding the tedium of trying everything that is possible. The heuristic process does not guarantee the answer as the algorithmic one does, but it saves a great deal of time when it works.

When the computer is made to simulate human thinking by building into it some of the things people are known to do, we can, in fact, learn more about human thinking by seeing how well our model works. There are computer programs that can solve problems picked directly from the calculus examinations at M.I.T., and can make derivations of the kind found in Whitehead and Russell's *Principia Mathematica* (1925). An extension of computer simulation beyond solving of the logical or game type of problem has been made to the field of personality. For example, one of my colleagues, Dr. Kenneth M. Colby, is testing the psychoanalytic theory of dreams by means of a computer program. This is not as bizarre as it sounds, and the studies of various psychological problems by means of computer simulation are bound to be among the exciting developments of the next few years.

The mathematical type of model, which need not be computer-based has already achieved such stature that we have a multi-volume *Handbook of Mathematical Psychology,* (Bush, Galanter & Luce, 1964) and a number of shorter texts. A forthcoming one, by Atkinson, Bower, and Crothers (1965) can be recommended as a useful introduction.

SOCIAL PSYCHOLOGY

In order to select a limited topic within this large domain, I wish to say something about models of attitude change, for social attitudes and their modifications have long been part of social psychology and are likely to remain so. Attitudes are closely related to our choice of friends, to our political actions and to other interpersonal problems. A useful review of several models of attitude change has been given by Brown (1962). He points out that through these models some of the facts of social psychology have fallen into compelling patterns that justify their status as basic science. The theories which he considers are all varieties of imbalance theory, which states, in essence, that as human beings we abhor incongruities, dissonances, and imbalances, and make any number of maneuvers in order to restore balance or unity. Hence attitudes change when by changing them balance can be restored. The general idea behind such a theory, as behind most good psychological theory, has a great deal of justification in common experience; what makes the theory scientific is its precision, so that a choice can be made between equally plausible alternatives.

Pressures to change attitudes can be provided in various ways, by arguments, by incentives, and so on. I wish to discuss one experiment in which hypnosis was used (Rosenberg, 1960). The attitudes of subjects toward several controversial topics were first determined, such as labor's right to strike, more conciliatory attitudes of the U.S. toward the U.S.S.R., and comprehensive Federal medical insurance. Then efforts were made to change cognitive attitudes through a change in affect, half to become more favorable than they began, half to become more negative to the proposition involved within each issue. The change was attempted under hypnosis for half the subjects, in the waking condition for the other half. The results were strikingly in favor of modification under the hypnotic condition. In a later experiment (in this case the issue was the foreign aid program of the United States) the changed attitude persisted over a week through posthypnotic suggestion, with amnesia for the fact that the change had been made within hypnosis. The change not only endured for this time, but showed some persistance for at least 10 days after removal of the amnesia. These persistent changes were apparently due to a kind of "self-convincing" that went on in arguing for the new attitude while under the influence of the posthypnotic suggestion. We see here an experiment concerned with attitude-change as a basic-science problem, but obviously there are practical suggestions that emerge, even perhaps a bit frightening.

I hope that I have thus far given some of the flavor of psychology as a biological science, as a somewhat independent science building its own models, making use of mathematics and computer simulation, and as a social science, dealing with problems of human attitudes and interactions.

PSYCHOLOGY AS AN APPLIED SCIENCE

To turn now to psychology as a technology, as something useful, I shall use as my samples personality tests, programed learning, psychotherapy, and persuasive techniques.

PERSONALITY TESTS

Questions have been raised about the ethics of testing (e.g., Gross, 1962), usually implying that the tests are inefficient as well as immoral; they might be thought of as more immoral if they were more efficient, for then the test-score label might be attached to an individual as firmly as his finger-prints and raise the same problems of preserving his right to privacy.

In some respects the most interesting problems lie in the field of personality measurement. We know that more men lose their jobs because of poor human relations than because of lack of skill, so that personality appraisal is, in fact, very important for job placement. A personality test differs from an intelligence test in two important respects:

1. First, it is designed to test one's characteristic mode of responding, not necessarily what one does when on good behavior. Intelligence tests, on the other hand, seek to know the best one can do when he is paying attention and trying hard. Thus a person may know that it is wise to be courteous to people and to show respect to superiors, but this does not mean that this will be his character-

istic behavior. On a personality test a person may be asked: "Do you sometimes feel just miserable?" To answer this question he has to decide whether or not this is characteristic of him and not answer on the basis of one experience in which he felt miserable when he nearly drowned as a child.

2. Second, there are no objective standards by which to judge the goodness or badness of any single answer. On an intelligence test a good answer always corresponds with truth and fact, and the main problem of the test constructor is to order the questions for difficulty. Then a bright persons answers more questions correctly than a dull one. But with personality it is not so simple. "Do you blush easily?" "Do you get angry at people who disagree with you?" Questions of this sort, which may in fact distinguish one group of people from another, do not have the direct validation that intellectual items do. Depending on degree, some blushing may be attractive, and some anger may be a fitting protest. Too much blushing may be embarrassing, and too much anger may make one ineffective. It is only that the problem of the test constructor is a difficult one.

For these two reasons, then, personality tests have not had the smooth sailing of intelligence tests. Because of the uncertainty with respect to when to reply to questions worded as "often," or "sometimes," considerable recent discussion has centered upon stylistic aspects of response to personality inventories. That is, the answers may reflect not so much the actual content of the questions as the ways in which they are asked. The two dimensions that emerge most frequently are social desirability and acquiescence (Holtzman, 1965). Social desirability refers to the tendency to answer the question in the way that is recognized as socially desirable or healthy. Thus a subject usually knows it would be socially undesirable to feel nauseated or to be unable to sleep at night or to walk across the street to avoid meeting somebody. Hence he has strong leanings in the direction of giving the conforming response, unless he is indeed sick enough to be asking for help. One reason these tests work to some extent in a clinical population is that these help-seeking people do indeed reveal themselves on the test. In addition to the tendency to social conformity is a tendency to say "yes" more readily than to say "no." This is called an acquiescence tendency; suggestible people are likely to be yea-sayers or yes-men, and thus to corrupt their scores.

Various difficulties with personality tests have led to the notion that perhaps a simple adding-up of responses, a method that worked for intelligence, will not work for personality tests. We have shown in our own research on hynosis, for example, that there are alternative paths into hypnosis, and a number of moderate scores on the several paths are not the equal, for purposes of predicting hypnotizability, of a high score on a single relevant one (Hilgard, 1965).

PROGRAMED INSTRUCTION

Although the educational psychology of learning lagged somewhat in the last decades, this situation has been corrected in part by the development of teaching machines and programed instruction. Between 1954, when B. F. Skinner first announced programed learning, and 1958 some 25 research reports appeared; between the years 1960 and 1964, the trickle of reports became a small flood, with some 165 research reports appearing (Schramm, 1964). This has continued, and programed learning in its various forms is now the basis for a large industry as well as for a large research enterprise.

Without going into technical details, programed learning has some of the following advantages that appeal to investigators interested in the psychology of learning:

1. It recognizes *individual differences* by beginning where the learner is, and permitting him to move at his own rate.

2. It requires the learner to be *active.*

3. It provides immediate feedback in the form of *knowledge of results,* thus favoring learning the right thing and avoiding the retention of errors.

4. It emphasizes the *organized nature of knowledge* because it requires continuity between the easier (earlier) concepts and the harder (later) ones.

5. It provides *spaced review* in order to guarantee retention of what has been learned.

6. It reduces anxiety and frustration, because the learner can always be successful at some level, and *he knows that he is learning.*

These plausible advantages favor the general strategy of programed learning, but they do not dictate the details, and research is needed to determine what features make for the most effective programs. The initial advantage that was thought to rest in the machine because of its precise timing of feedback turned out not to be supported by experimental data, the programed book doing as well as the machine in tryout. Many other research problems have been faced, such as size of step, form of reply, and so on, with a good deal of useful information accumulating.

Rather than go further into all of this, we may well ask: "What of the future? Where is this taking us?"

The hope that simple programs would produce dramatic changes in the efficiency of teaching is hardly borne out, so that the program is little likely to supplant the teacher. Instead the program is likely to take its place alongside other educational aids that have appeared from time to time: blackboards, notebooks, laboratories, libraries, textbooks, field-trips, discussion groups, and audiovisual aids of other kinds.

The one area where a revolution may indeed occur, and programing is involved in this, is computer-based instruction. A number of significant experiments are now going on or getting under way in which a whole classroom is tied to a single computer, but each pupil works at his own speed, gets the information that he needs, knows when he is right and when he is wrong, and is helped to review as necessary, all through the flexibility of the computer. At the same time a complete record of his responses, right and wrong, is stored in the computer, which concurrently may be accumulating statistics on the whole class so that at any time a "readout" will tell the supervising instructor exactly what progress is being made and which students are in trouble. Not even a group of individual tutors could give such close supervision to the learning process. While the costs at present are quite high, this is due chiefly to the developmental costs in getting the programs together and the machinery in operation; even at the present cost of computers, once everything is running, the cost per pupil hour is not much different from present instructional costs.

PSYCHOTHERAPY

As everybody knows, the great name in this area has been that of Sigmund Freud, the founder of psychoanalysis, a man of undoubted genius and one of the great names of the last 100 years, to be thought of in the company of Darwin, Einstein, and Pavlov. We are witnessing in the 1960's a curious fading of Freud's reputation, a repudiation of his theories, and attacks upon the psychotherapeutic methods that he proposed. The spirit of the times, the *Zeitgeist,* has for some reason become less favorable to his views. This is scarcely a matter of evidence one way or the other, for the same kind of evidence has been lying around all along, with the same division of opinion over it. We are perhaps too close to what is happening to feel very secure in interpreting it, but I shall do the best I can. It will be recalled that Freud's theory is essentially a psychogenic theory of neurosis, that is, a theory that neurosis has psychological causes through conflicts generated in the lifetime of the individual. The cure is also psychological, by way of free associations and the interpretations provided by the psychoanalyst. The psychogenic kind of interpretation meets opposition at this time from the advance in biochemistry and genetics. The tranquilizers seemed (at least for a time) more potent than counseling as a way to help the troubled, although we now know that the placebo-effect had a good deal to do with it, so we cannot escape some psychological aspects of therapy. The advances of genetics and the concept of molecular disease now offer many possibilities for the organic basis for illness. Once this enthusiasm rises, all psychogenic theories become suspect, and the Freudian theory suffers along with others. This, then, is one root for the decline of Freud's prestige.

Another root of the attack upon Freud, quite different from this, is the rise of alternative psychotherapies. These do not question the psychogenesis of conflict, anxiety, and other symptoms of neurosis. Most commonly they attribute the symptoms to learning and cure them through learning. These behavior therapies, as they are called, have many varieties, but the two that at present are most in vogue are a desensitization theory called by its originator psychotherapy by reciprocal inhibition (Wolpe, 1958), and a verbal conditioning therapy, in which through the reinforcement of some kinds of statements by the subject and extinction of others his attitudes toward himself and the world become changed and he functions more adequately (Krasner, 1965). According to London (1964) the contrast is between insight therapy of the Freudian variety and action therapy of the newer types. His own preference is for an integration of what has been learned from both.

This head-on conflict between the biochemical and the psychogenic theories of the origin of problems, and of the chemical vs. insight vs. action treatment of the problems themselves is likely to stir up energetic new efforts to arrive at a consensus that can dictate appropriate practice.

There are many justifications for an eclectic position, despite the confidence of some who hold dogmatically to one or another extreme view, assembling data to show that they are reasonable men. As one illustration, consider the postpartum psychosis which unfortunately is not too uncommon among young mothers. There are such pronounced hormonal changes associated with pregnancy and childbirth that it is not surprising to find the system put under strain, and this makes plausible a biochemical or hormonal theory of the postpartum reaction in susceptible women. Yet careful studies show similar reactions when a new baby comes into the home on the part of two kinds of people to whom the hormone theory does not apply: to the father, who may protect himself somewhat from his symptoms by running away from home when the child is born or by taking to alcohol, and by the mother who has a similar psychotic reaction when she finds herself confronted with a new baby that she has adopted. Who is to say what is chemical and what is psychogenic?

Persuasive Techniques

My final specimen of applied psychology comes from the fields of motivation and social psychology. I speak of the psychology of persuasion. There are many ways in which we attempt to manipulate other people, in persuading them to vote for our candidates, or for a bond issue for the schools, in persuading them to buy our products. In psychological warfare we may wish to persuade them to acts of sabotage against their own people, to defect from the ranks, to weaken the will to fight. Obviously we are in an important area of applied social psychology. As an illustration I wish to cite a fairly benign use of persuasion, that appears to have turned out successfully.

In our modern world, a high degree of industrialization appears imperative to support a high standard of living, and such industrialization appears to depend upon arousing in people what has been called the need for achievement, a motive very important in any society based upon enterprise. Careful analysis by McClelland has shown the relationship between this motive and the rise of capitalism in European countries (McClelland, 1961). As we now become interested in helping developing nations to industrialize, we need to do more than to send money and technicians to build dams and to provide machinery. We have also to develop motives appropriate to this kind of society.

McClelland, adopting the position that I have indicated, wondered if he could help people in India to help themselves by encouraging the development of a need for achievement on the part of small businessmen in that country. He has recently reported the results of his efforts. (McClelland, 1965). What McClelland did was to hypothesize that motives could be changed in adult life, and then he took principles from animal learning, human learning, human psychotherapy, and studies of attitude-change to design short courses (lasting 1-3 weeks) to be given to groups of businessmen, designed to increase their achievement motives. These have now been given for several years to managers or teachers of management in the United States, Mexico, and India. In India, for example, of 82 businessmen who were studied, some 20 had demonstrated high achievement motivation by unusual entrepreneurial activity during the two years prior to the short course. Within the two years after the course, however, 54 of the 82 engaged in such activity, a significant increase.

These practical results are of the kind that various "inspirational" courses have claimed in the past. The difference is that in McClelland's work the hypotheses are carefully spelled out and careful appraisal measures are used. Therefore his work can contribute to basic psychology in the way in which the previous unscientific work cannot, valuable as some of it may have been in itself.

SUMMARY AND PERSPECTIVE

I hope that I may have succeeded in giving some samples of psychologists at work in the spirit of both basic and applied science, indicating the vitality of the field and its current breadth. At the same time I have tried to show that there really is not so very much difference between basic and applied research when both are good science, and that, in fact, they mutually interact. Without basic research, the applications would often be bumbling and uncritical; without the technological tryouts important areas of investigation might have their basic problems overlooked, and a neat narrowness persist where a somewhat less neat breadth is more appropriate to the problems to be solved.

REFERENCES

Atkinson, R. C., Bower, G. H., and Crothers, E. J. (1965). *An introduction to mathematical learning theory.* New York: Wiley.

Brown, R. (1962). Models of attitude change. In *New directions in psychology.* New York: Holt, Rinehart, and Winston, 1-85.

Bush, R. R., Galanter, E., & Luce, R. D. (1964). *Handbook of mathematical psychology.* New York: Wiley.

Gross, M. L. (1962). *The brain watchers.* New York: Random House.

Hilgard, E. R. (1965). *Hypnotic susceptibility.* New York: Harcourt, Brace, & World.

Hirsch, J. & Boudreau, J. C. (1958). Studies in experimental behavior genetics: I. The heritability of phototaxis in a population of drosophila melanogaster. *J. comp. physiol. Psychol.,* 51, 647-651.

Holtzman, W. (1965) Personality structure. *Ann. Review of Psychol.,* 16, 119-156.

Krasner, L. (1965) Verbal conditioning and psychotherapy. In Krasner, L., and Ullman, L. P. (Eds.) *Research in behavior modification.* New York: Holt, Rinehart & Winston, 211-228.

Landauer, T. K. & Whiting, J. M. W. (1964) Infant stimulation and adult stature of human males. *American Anthropologist,* 66, 1007-1028.

Levine, S. J. (1962). Psychophysiological effects of infant stimulation. In E. L. Bliss (Ed.) *Roots of behavior.* New York: Hoeber.

London, P. (1964) *The modes and morals of psychotherapy.* New York: Holt, Rinehart & Winston.

McClelland, D. C. (1961) *The achieving society.* Princeton, N. J.: Van Nostrand.

McClelland, D. C. (1965) Toward a theory of motive acquisition. *Amer. Psychologist,* 20, 321-333.

Mayr, E. (1958). Behavior and systematics. In Roe, Anne and Simpson, G. G. (Eds.) *Behavior and evolution.* New Haven: Yale Univ. Press, 341-362.

Rogers, C. R., and Skinner, B. F. (1956) Some issues concerning the control of human behavior. *Science,* 124, 1057-1066.

Rosenberg, M. J. (1960) Cognitive reorganization in response to the hypnotic reversal of attitudinal affect. *J. Pers.,* 28, 39-63.

Schramm, W. (1964) *The research on programmed instruction: An annotated bibliography.* Washington, D. C.: U. S. Office of Education (OE-34034).

Whitehead, A. N. & Russell, B. (1925). *Principia mathematica* (2nd Ed.) Cambridge, England: Cambridge University Press.

Wolpe, J. (1958) *Psychotherapy by reciprocal inhibition.* Stanford, Calif.: Stanford Univ. Press.

VI. Living Models For Lively Artifacts

Warren S. McCulloch

I am used to talking to audiences made up of biologists and engineers, but I am told that many of you are physicists, chemists and geologists. So, though I will say nothing new, I must say it differently and I think I had better do it in two parts — the first biology, and the second engineering. We will first consider how real brains work and then how they have inspired us to make devices to do similar things. This is the natural order and roughly corresponds to the historical order.

Biology as a science really began with the ancient Greek city-states and sprang largely from using ideas of how they ran themselves to account for living things, themselves included.

Perhaps the most important of these is the notion of the bound cause. In physics we lack it, and suppose all the conditions that determine an event to be its cause. The notion of a bound cause, or natural cause, is very useful. If I look for your parents, I need only to seek among human beings, not among the birds and butterflies. If I want to know how come you are here, I need not know whether you came by car or bus. And if some came late, I'm sure the cause was accidental, not a bound cause, merely a casual one.

The first was an example of Biological Law, that like begets like; notice, not quite the same.

The second brings in the notion of purpose. In physics, things happen or else they don't happen. But in biology and in engineering, things must work or they cease to exist, and signals must be true or we cease to attend to them. In short, you are now considering

WARREN S. McCULLOCH, physician and psychiatrist, is head of the neurophysiology group at the Research Laboratory of Electronics, Massachusetts Institute of Technology. Drs. McCulloch, Wiener, Ashby, and Grey were responsible for the founding of the science of cybernetics. Dr. McCulloch is an AFOSR grantee in Information Sciences.

a world in which there are values, utilities, purposes and propositions. Organisms are composed of organs as machines are made of
components. These parts must serve the whole, each in its own way.
This is their function. This is like the members of a city. The ship-
wrights must build the boats for the fishermen, and the fishermen
must catch fish or the city starves. This leads to the next great law,
called the equality of unequals. Since each is necessary to the state,
they must be equal under the law; and this notion of a law—that
there are to be no exceptions—is the origin of the notion of a law in
physics as well as in every science.

If every citizen did exactly the same thing, the city would perish.
This specialization of function is most obvious in matters of sex, for
if we were all male or all female, we would beget no children.

The Greeks supposed that the man injected the woman with a
material that informed her with what she was to grow. They called
it a perfect mixture, and thought of it much as an engineer thinks
of a correct program. It is the natural cause of the computation.
But the program, being on a physical tape that may be accidentally
wrongly punched or torn, may produce a wrong answer, or, in generation, a misshapen offspring.

Empedocles says the world is created by love and strife. Love
brings together the unlike, male and female, shipwright and fisher-
man, whereas, when the carpenters line up on one side and the
fishermen on the other, there is faction in the state—internal war.

The Greeks thought of knowledge as a coming together of the
knower and the unlike known as, in the biblical sense, a man is said
to know a woman. The fulls of the one fill the empties of the other,
as when a hand grasps an object; hence our word to apprehend or
comprehend, or the simple English, I grasp your meaning. And the
Greeks believed that in the act of grasping some of the atoms of
the known, its earth, air, fire and water in their proper proportions,
passed to the knower, where they entered his blood, becoming
mixed in veins and finally in his heart. I have had many patients
who believed they thought with their blood, but I believe the last
time I heard a physician think that way was some 40 years ago, when
the neurosurgeon, Dandy, said he knew to his cost that consciousness
was in the left anterior cerebral artery. The net of our veins resembles the mouth of the Danube, where many streams come to-

gether in a flood plane and mix their waters in many intersecting channels, so that water in any one mouth has water from every river. The Greek for this is "anastomosis." Except for hormones and antibodies, we have transferred our theories of knowing from blood to brain, where we have the proper anastomotic net. It is neither a series nor a parallel circuit—no more so than a Wheatstone Bridge that cannot be so analyzed.

It was Alcmaeon of Croton who seems to have been the first to attribute perception to the brain; that was about 450 B.C. Based on his surgical experience, he thought the eyes made the opposites, light-dark, etc., and shipped them to the brain, where they mixed harmoniously to produce knowledge in the healthy man. Hundreds of years later, in Alexandria, the anatomists made a clear picture of the brain and nerves, but that information was lost until the Renaissance in Italy. Only in the last 75 years have we come to realize that a brain is not a mass of jelly in which fibers precipitated, but is actually a host of separate cells, whose thin processes are the fibers. This is the neuronal hypothesis of Ramon y Cajal, who divides the cells of the brain into the information handling neurons that stain with silver, and the supporting cells, or glea, which are the wet nurses of the neurons and do not stain with silver.

A human brain weighs about three pounds and has a blood flow of about a quart per minute—that's about one-seventh of your circulation. It heats that quart of blood about one degree Fahrenheit, that is, about 25 watts, and this is the same, waking or sleeping. Only in epileptic fits does it use much more energy. The brain floats in cerebro-spinal fluid, which has the same density. Its pH is about 7.2, which is very stable except in fits.

The brain gets its energy from burning sugar, glucose to be exact, and neurons die in about three minutes if their oxygen supply is cut off. It ferments the sugar to pyruvic acid, but cannot live unless this is burnt to CO_2 and H_2O. This burning is coupled with the building up of adenocine triphosphate, which is the source of its energy, just as it is in muscle. It stores this energy in phospho-creatine, and the store is constant except in convulsions, when it is greatly depleted. Nearly a hundred diseases of the nervous system have been traced to definite metabolic disorders. But we may all forget all of this and consider the brain in good working order and with a constant supply of energy, for we are only concerned with how it handles information—for that is its function.

Let me get one more thing out of the way. If the Greek city-state was to survive, it had to have one more law—"General because first" or "General because best." If the state is to survive, the best man has to lead and the best decision has to be made. Then all have to agree. This is a precursor of the Darwinian notion of the survival of the fittest determining evolution, and it is crucial in decision-making and in learning, as opposed to mere memorizing or conditioning. Neither for decisions nor for learning have we anything approaching a decent neurological theory, and I shall later describe this problem.

At least three things are called memory. One is persistent activity in the nervous system. This lasts like sea-legs or dizziness after spinning. In old age, it may be all we have when we can no longer make new traces. Bilateral lesions of a part of the old cortex, called the hypocampus, produce this difficulty, leaving us clear memories of earlier days.

If we are to make new traces, there must be some change in structure. This takes time, before which there must be some persistent activity of some sort—probably electrical and lasting probably minutes, some think for half an hour. The structural change must be such as to affect the transmission of signals. Presumably this means that a structural material like protein must be made, and this requires an increase of a template for making it—called ribose nucleic acid. This is known to occur. Some think that the information is due to the structure of the protein produced, as it is in the development of antibodies. Others think it may be just more protein to be shipped to some specific part of the neuron. No one yet knows. Growth with use and atrophy with disease are common properties of many tissues. We would expect them in the learning of skilled acts in brain as in brawn.

The third thing called memory seems to consist of successive snapshots, at about 10 per second, that we can review in the original sequence, not in reverse. These we use in reconstructing a crime or accident. I have no idea how it works. It has been best studied in the memorizing of nonsense syllables, and the mean half-life of such stuff is about half a day. The half-life makes it possible to guess at the energy barrier that must be jumped, and from this come various estimations of the amount stored. Heinz von Foerster has proved it is energetically no great matter, a fraction of what the brain uses. The estimates are some 10^{12} to 10^{15} bits, large for even a large computer store. So much for memory! We think much of it is stored in many places, probably chiefly in the forebrain. Simple location is certainly wrong. It's not like a random access to something like a magnetized core. It may well be distributed as in a hologram. We don't yet know how or where.

Before we come to the detail of the component neurons, their connection and interactions, let me describe grossly the whole central nervous system. It consists of a brain and spinal cord. The biggest bulge is at the front end of the forebrain, consisting of a bark or cortex, whose business is to take those habits that give us perceptions, ideas, conceptions, etc. Deep to the cortex is the antiroom or thalamus, where signals coming from elsewhere than the cortex are gated and relayed to the cortex. And then deeper sits the upper portion of the so-called basal ganglia, whose business is to program our actions as in walking, eating, dancing and swimming. Behind the forebrain is the midbrain, which handles more automatic movement and receives and preprocesses information from receptors for acceleration and audition, taste and touch. In lower forms, it handles everything except smell, but in us it has lost its visual function proper, though it still has an input from the eyes and directs our gaze. Finally, we come to the hindbrain, which has a huge bulge on its back called the cerebellum, which has an interval clock used in making precise our ballistic acts by stopping at the right place whatever is put in motion. Since it's tapped everywhere, it can be used for autocorrelating signals up out of noise, and it is used exaggeratedly by the weak electric fish, who can detect a one-millimeter glass rod at a distance of one meter in brackish water.

Throughout its length, the nervous system can be divided into a sensory plate on the back, a motor plate on the front, and a reticulum, or net of neurons, between them. All the specialized computers of the brain, cerebral cortex, thalamus, basal ganglia, cerebellum, etc., have evolved out of the reticulum. If every input had been connected to every reticular cell and every reticular cell to every motor neuron, as well as every reticular cell to every reticular cell, then the specialized computers could be made by omitting some connections. Actually the connections were never that rich. The core of the reticulum has not evolved. Its business is to make those decisions that commit the whole organism to one of some 20 of those acts with short English names—eat, sleep, fight, flight, etc. In segmented animals, including us, it is clearly an iterated net. The theory of such nets is such that it can be shown, and has been by Hennie and Kilmer, that every question we would like to ask concerning its activity is recursively insoluble. Kilmer and I are still after it. It is the command and control system that has and still does enable us to survive. It enjoys a redundancy of potential command in which information constitutes authority. It is a population of a few million cells so related that whatever cluster of neurons knows what has to be done can sweep the rest into harmonious activity.

So much for the grand scheme. Now for the details beginning with the components, the neurons. Each is a living creature having a body, branches and a tap root, called an axon. Normally the branches and body receive signals and the axon passes them to other neurons or, if motor neurons, to muscles and glands. The membrane surrounding the cell and axon has a capacity ranging from 1 μF at least to about 40 μF at most. It is composed of a double layer of phospholipids made into a sort of insoluble soap by calcium sitting at the junction of the layers. Metabolism maintains a voltage through this membrane, about 1/10 volt positive outside. So long as the voltage remains, the resistance is high; but when it is forced down by about 1/3 of its resting value, the calcium ion gets out of the way and sodium rushes in; then potassium leaks out and the voltage overshoots to negative outside. Then the sodium is pumped out and the potassium leaks back. The equations for this were worked out by Hodgkin and Huxley a decade ago. By nuclear magnetic resonance, it is easy to show that the bulk of water in whole brain is bound in a somewhat icy state. The sodium ion will not fit in such a lattice and must be extruded as it is from frozen seawater; hence the sodium pump. Potassium fits and can diffuse either way under the force of the electrical field; hence the potassium leaks. Lettvin and his coworkers have shown that the crucial actions on nerve membrane of all ions whose shell of water is known are determined by that shell. Calcium^{++} is replaced by lanthanum^{+++}, whose water shell is like it but whose valence is 3 instead of 2. It prevents the nervous impulse from occurring and, being radio-opaque, has given us a new stain for ultra-miscroscopy, which shows its location in the membrane.

The properties of the hydrated potassium ion as to size, mobility, etc., resemble those of cesium, which has no water shell. Nerve membrane pays no attention to cesium. For these and several other reasons, one can be sure that the nerve impulse is not to be explained simply by solution chemistry.

When a cell body becomes sufficiently depolarized, the near part of its axon suddenly depolarizes. This trips the next portion and it, in turn forces the next. This is the propagated all-or-none nervous impulse whose velocity of transmission depends upon the distributed resistance, distributed capacitance and distributed battery, as you would expect in a distributed repeater. Seen from the surrounding medium, it is a traveling sink of current preceded by a source whither it is going and followed by a source whence it came. Even at a small lateral distance in the surrounding conductors, its effect is vastly attenuated, thus reducing cross-talk. Excitation of a cell is produced only by an inwardly directed current (Na^+). Inhibition can be produced either by hyperpolarizing the axonal end, in which case it is subtractive, or by a shunt (K^+), in which case it is divisive. Both we know to occur. It was the latter that Lettvin used to explain his algorism, relating the form to the function of neurons. What led him to it was that he was able to identify the function computed by each of 4 varieties of ganglion cells of the frog's eye from a careful anatomical study of the connectivity and dimensions of the bipolar and ganglion cells. So we can guess function from form and check it rapidly, because the test is usually appropriate. Finally, note that a neuron is not a simple threshold device, like a flip-flop. It sends trains of impulses whose figure in time carries the message—sometimes the mere number, sometimes the repetition rate, perhaps in some places the pulse intervals themselves. From a logical point of view it can compute at least every boolean function. With only a threshold device with just two inputs, the function of "if and only if" and "the one or else the other" cannot be constructed. Yet we have in the brain stem a collection of cells embodying the latter. They respond to signals from either ear but not from both. A beep in one ear 10 db below noise in that ear alone becomes audible with the same noise in both, and disappears when the beep is in both. It is these cells, working on phase differences, which enable us to tell its direction in the horizontal plane. This is best done with a click and, in the case of Prof. Van der Pol, he was good to one microsecond, whereas no neuron is good to $\pm$ 30 microseconds, either in sending or in detecting coincidence. This must have rested upon a vote of similar neurons that enjoyed the requisite variety. The anastomotic nature of nerve nets, the variation in the functions they compute, and escape from the confines of the strictly threshold component are all essential in the reliable computation in the presence of noise, as shown by Winograd and Cowan. Verveen has been measuring the noise in axons. It rises as it should with decrease of the diameter. For 6 microns, it is about a percent, and for the finest it exceeds a third of the threshold stimulus and hence must often fire them. For low frequencies, it is as you might expect, $1/F$, and for higher, white noise.

We grow no new neurons. They die in large numbers every hour, and the circuits must be designed so that losses of large numbers, either scattered or bunched, do not destroy our ability to perceive, think and act. The latter requires reduplication of receptors and effectors, as well as of nervous structures.

Finally, we can only survive by keeping many variables within limits. This we do by closed loops of negative feedback. These circuits exist within the central nervous system, through it and the effector-receptor circuits, and through us and the world about us. The last mediate our appetites. So purpose as well as knowledge is the proper business of the brain. For the survival of our kind, we must communicate at least with others of our kind—hence our societies and our languages. We are beginning to know what parts of the cortex are especially requisite for them, how they mature, and what happens when they are severally destroyed, but not yet how they work. The pathological linguistic feedback in human communities produce the great disorders of societies, states and nations: schisms, factions, wars. Their normal behavior has given us logic, mathematics and science, and this is my next concern.

We come now to lively imitation of these living things, the beginning of communication engineering. The history of computers, digital ones, goes back to keeping tally by throwing calculi (pebbles) into pots and to the abacus. The history of logical machines began about 1200 with Lullian wheels. The greatest of the Lullians was Leibnitz, with his Universal Characteristic. He rightly says if you look inside a thinking, perceiving and caring machine, you will find only forms in motion, for his was mechanical. Let me skip the rest and come to Turing, who proved that a machine with a finite number of states, working on an infinite tape, able to scan one square, move one square, and make or erase a mark, could compute any number that a man could compute. What distinguishes his lively computer from all its predecessors is not merely that it is an automaton, but that it can make its next operation depend in part on the value of the operand. This, he saw, entailed that, given that there was any other source of marks appearing on the working tape, it had the possibility of induction as well as of the deduction inherent in arithmetic calculation. Inasmuch as Gödel had arithmetized logic, the calculation of all calculable numbers was equivalent to deducing every consequence of a finite set of postulates. In 1943, when Pitts and I proved that a proper set of neurons, stupid threshold neurons, could compute a host of numbers, making use of reverberating circuits for many of them, and given receptors and effectors with an infinite tape, could compute all numbers that a Turing machine could compute, this became equivalent to saying it could perceive any figures in its input. By 1947, we had a general theory of recognition of universals, such as a cord regardless of key, or a shape regardless of size.

This is particularly important today. William of Occan, who would never allow unnecessary entities to be postulated, insisted that man thought in two kinds of terms—one, natural terms enjoyed by other animals; the other, conventional terms, enjoyed by man alone. These are linguistic, logical terms, of which the greatest is number. Now the natural language of the computing machines is the conventional terms of man—notably numbers. It was for this that Turing had designed them. They think in number faster and more surely than we do. This is easily extended to logic and formal languages. What we had proved was that their use could be extended to perception of universals. They were not built for the task, and using them so takes a deal of programming. This paved the way for many an attempt at machine recognition of objects, tunes, "ham"-sent Morse code, sloppy handwritten letters, and machine evolving and machine learning.

Julian Bigelow realized that all a machine had to have was information of the outcome of previous acts in order to steer properly, even at a moving target. He, Wiener with his mathematics, and

Rosenbluth with his biology, in 1943 wrote the first article on teleology and mechanism, thus initiating what Wiener christened Cybernetics in his famous book in which he properly included the computer, whether in man or machine, for the appropriate handling of information. Thus these lively machines incorporate purposes as well as thinking and perceiving. We don't indulge in suicidal ventures lightly, and there is many a one-way trip on which we would be happier to send a machine than a man. There are environments so hostile and constraints of time, space and power, where a small digital computer, working in the nanosecond range instead of the millisecond range, weighing less, traveling faster and controlling more power than 1/10 horse, beats us with our 1/10-second brain and our 100-pound carcass. "Man is a dial twister and a tube snatcher—we must replace him." So said an admiral. Having spent years of lunches with Louis Sutro and coming to the conclusion that the hardware was yet to seek, a couple of years ago we said, "The time has come." We began working on artificial frogs' eyes because there we had best knowledge of a bug catcher and because, while the eye is more complicated, the brain is much simpler. Louis began the attempt for the Air Force and we are continuing it for NASA. I, as a biologist, want it to look down a microscope for crawling or swimming things on Mars; but it would be equally useful to spot sandstorms or moving monsters. Suppose the eye is built, and the simple computer behind it, called the "superior colliculus," with 4 maps in register, each of an appropriate function such as an advancing convex leading edge, an edge coming or going, etc.; the next problem is to build for it a reticular core to decide whether to transmit that picture, or store it, or discard it; to coordinate its movements, to adjust its scope or switch from micro- to telescope and look about, etc. We know nature does it, and therefore that we can. The great open problems are as follows. Today we swap space for time and use serial computers. Nature has beaten us at miniturizing —packing 10^{10} components in a single head so it can work "in parallel" and, having real neurons, not our poor threshold devices, in truly anastomotic nets combatting noise.

Theoretically we have the following troubles. We lack a theory for iterated decisional nets like the reticular core, and our mathematical symbolus for closed loop is as opaque as Roman numerals in long division; one operates on his subscripts instead of on his arguments.

We lack proper artificial neurons capable of computing any boolean function and so of being able to compose properly anastomotic nets to compute correctly in the presence of almost every kind of noise. Both Crane and Stewart are after this problem and hopefully one will succeed or they will get others so interested that someone will invent them—small, cheap, and growable in complex nets from simple prescription.

Perhaps some theorist among you might help us on the former problem, and certainly the latter is in your field.

VII. Theories of Memory

Julian H. Bigelow

In this presentation, the aim is to discuss the organizational aspects of memory, rather than the detailed mechanisms of elementary storage cells. As a reference framework, electrotechnological memory apparatus designed for electronic computers will be cited and described, because these can serve to illustrate many of the problems that are involved in the analysis of biological memories. They can especially reveal important differences that appear to distinguish the organization of man-made memory systems from those generated in nature.

Modern electronic calculating machines use memories that are constructed so as to provide large numbers of elementary cells, each cell being an element capable of being selectively forced to assume one of two (or more) distinguishable states. The rapidity with which the individual cell can be forced to assume a desired state is called the "flip" time, and has been shortened from about 10^{-3} seconds required for a very fast electromechanical device (of the era 1930-1940) to 10^{-6} seconds for standard electron tube devices (of the era 1940-1950) and still further to about 10^{-8} seconds for solid state elements of the era 1950-1960. In the decade 1960-1970 solid state thin-film techniques have lowered this time lapse to the range of 10^{-9} seconds, and it is possible that 10^{-10} may be feasible in the 1965-1975 era. However, with regard to flip-time it is clear that the rate of speed-up is now lagging the gain factor of one-thousand-fold per ten years characteristic of the earlier progress. The reason for this is quite clearly the intervention of factors other than the solid state physics of the memory cell itself, and that these other complicating

JULIAN H. BIGELOW is a permanent member of the Institute for Advanced Study in Princeton, New Jersey, having been appointed in 1953. He is the former head of the Electronic Computer Design Group at Princeton under Dr. John Von Neumann. Dr. Bigelow collaborated with Dr. Norbert Wiener in studies of prediction theory for use in weapons fire control that became the foundation of the field of cybernetics.

factors are directly related to delays in the wiring and switching means by which an individual cell is selected for access.

One answer to this "overhead burden" of wiring delays and means of access has been to make individual memory storage cells smaller and smaller. Whereas electromechanical relays of thousandth-second flip, and electron tubes of millionth-second flip were capable of storing from one to ten two-state pieces of information ("bits") per cubic centimeter of volume, modern solid state devices can store better than 100, and thin film devices better than 10,000 bits per cubic centimeter.[8] However, as the size of the memory cells has become smaller and their packing per unit volume very much greater, the difficulties of accessing them by wires and selective switching have remained a limiting factor in size and speed, and despite great ingenuity devoted to the problem, have not been condensed as effectively.

It therefore remains true that the design of an electronic calculating machine, built from the most up-to-date miniaturized cell-components, using the most sophisticated solid state bistable properties known to date, turns out to be a frustrating wrestling-match with problems of interconnectability and proximity in three dimensions of space and one dimension of time. Often more hours are spent on this than on the formal logical designing of the system, and on the achievement of the extraordinary miniaturization and quickness of state change in the individual elements involved.

One way of gaining insight into the reason that modern electronic computer designers find themselves in this sort of a log-jam is by observing that most known and understood calculating processes that can be expressed by "programming" are essentially serial. Therefore, in effect, only one thing is going on in the computer at a time, each step being (or at least subject to being) conditionally dependent on those preceding it, so that essential steps usually cannot be carried out independently or concurrently. From many points of view, there appear to be reasons to believe that this serially-dependent property of modern computer calculations cannot entirely be eliminated by any conceivable means but, on the other hand, may often be greatly reduced by reconsidering the statement of the problem and the catalogue of algorithms conceptually suitable for its solution. Another way of sketching the same difficulty and avoidance tactic is to point out that electronic computers follow instructions very rapidly, so that they "eat up" instructions very rapidly, and therefore some way must be found of forming batches of instructions very efficiently, and of "tagging" them efficiently, so that the computer is kept effectively busier than the programmer. This may seem like a highly whimsical way of characterizing a logically deep question of how to express computations to machines. However, it is believed to be not far from an important central truth, that highly recursive, conditional and repetitive routines are used because they are notationally efficient (but not necessarily unique) as descriptions of underlying processes.

In any event, serial order along the time axis is the customary method of carrying out computations today, although it is by no means clear that this choice of a preferred coordinate in representational procedures is either advantageous or necessary.* One result of this choice is a highly specialized functional separation of the logically distinct components of the computing apparatus, namely memory here control there, operation (arithmetic) unit there (etc.) with many resulting nuisance problems of effecting a flow of the calculational process through the bottlenecks of the apparatus. In consequence, it can be said that the modern high speed computer, impressive as its performance is from the point of view of absolute accomplishment, is from the point of view of getting the available logical equipment adequately engaged in the computation, very inefficient indeed. Thus thousands of very refined logical elements are built, each capable of making a "flip" to store or divulge a bit of information (or equivalently to make a logical gating decision) at a very fast rate for which great premium is paid, and then they are interconnected in such a way that on the average almost all of them are waiting for one (or a very few of their number) to act. Expressed differently, the average duty cycle of each cell is scandalously low, often being in

---

* Of course, certain physical phenomena—notably those described by thermodynamic relations—involve descriptions giving preferred treatment to events ordered in time. But in forming any model of real world processes for study in a computer, there seems no reason why this must be initiated by pairing computer-time-sequences with physical time parameters of the real-world model. In general, it should also be possible to trace backward or forward from results to causes through any path-representation of the process. It would seem that the time-into-time convention ordinarily used is due to the fact that humans interpreting the results of a computation and matching these with observations on physical phenomena are accustomed to working in coordinates that are, so to speak, "egocentric."

the range of one act in ten thousand to a million possible action-occasions.

A second result of the habitual serial-time sequence mode and of the large number of candidate cells waiting to participate in the computation at the next opportunity, if it becomes their turn, is the emergence of a particularly difficult identification problem. Thus the requirement of an efficient tagging scheme for accessing the cells contributing to a calculation looms large because of the need to address an arbitrary next candidate, and to know where it is in machine-space. Of course, it can be said that to the extent that the next candidate participating in the calculation is unpredictable, explicit addressing of that cell is an irremovable requirement of the system design. But it is also true that these parameters descriptive of a given computational process on a given system of apparatus tend today to be more nearly the result of chance circumstance rather than of design. In short, for man-made electronic computers, a practice adopted, whereby events are represented with serial dependence in time, has resulted in computing apparatus that must be built of elements that are, to a large extent, strictly independent across space-dimensions. This has led to the choice of a preferred mode of bringing into play these computing elements by means of explicit systems of tags characterizing the basically irrelevant geometric properties of the apparatus, known as "addresses." Then accomplishment of the desired time-sequential process on a given computing apparatus turns out to be largely a matter of specifying sequences of addresses of items which are to interact.*

Within the community of specialists in the design of modern high speed electronic calculating machines, and of experts in preparing and formulating calculational problems to be exercised on such machines, there recently has been general recognition of the impediment raised by this time-serial limitation on computation. Also recognized has been the burden of explicit addressing as sole means for introducing connectivities between computational elements, such as those stored in the "memory" cells of the machine, and the computationally active assemblies of the equipment (arithmetic units, etc.). It has been realized that other methods and techniques may conceivably be workable, even for some classes of conventional prob-

---

* In a more abstract form, the problem outlined here is related to certain aspects of the modern theories of automata, of switching and of sequential machines.

lem formulation and program representation. In an effort to avoid the "strictly serial" computational blockade in the physical hardware of the actual machine, various attempts at introducing logical parallelism in the design of arithmetic units and other major units have been explored. The ideas of Holland,[4] Slotnick et al[11] and of Aoki and Estrin[1] represent significant approaches to better distribution of the logical calculating load represented by different complex problems over the calculating capabilities of the processor configuration. Methods of representing calculations with reference to their separability into independent and sequentially dependent parts by means of topological tools have been explored by Karp and Miller.[5] Anticipatory control systems designed to "look-ahead" of the present stage of a calculating process so as to bring together the probably-needed future constituents, and in some cases to partially precalculate it, have also been studied, and in some cases reduced to more or less effective practice. Computation by successive partially-complete stages has also been studied. Unfortunately, all these schemes lead to inconclusive estimates of effectiveness because of lack of any general penetration of the underlying logical problems of representing the basic processes; clearly this leads into very deep water.

With regard to the explicit address nuisance, studies have been made of the possibility of causing various elementary pieces of information situated in the cells of a large array (say, of memory) to enter into a computational process without explicitly generating a coordinate address in "machine-space" for selecting them out of the array and thereafter introducing them into the active phases of the computation. Usually these schemes are called "content addressable memories" or "associative memories" or the like. They have been proposed and studied by Slade,[10] Petersen et al,[12] Fuller[2] and many others. In general, the results have been to indicate feasibility, but that the additional circuit logic necessary to be associated with each cell of memory tends to be prohibitively large. As a result what would be accomplished amounts to distribution of large amounts of arithmetic logic throughout the whole, or some appreciable part, of the memory system. If not used in a very efficient fashion, such schemes tend to end up by increasing the overall amount of logical equipment resting in an idle state rather than reducing it, although clearly the system can handle certain types of search operation at very high rate. It would seem that two distinct types of advance are needed to make this scheme more effective: first, a better characterization of the circumstances under which it is to be used, along with efficient representation of this in terms of the massive logical operations provided, and second, a better understanding of ways to combine storage and interpretive logic more efficiently.

Summarizing to this point, the problems of achieving suitable memory capabilities in high speed, man-made computing machines have been sketchily reviewed to provide a set of background ideas, concepts and terminology suitable for discussing other more general types of memory organization problems, namely those of biological systems and particularly of man. It should be emphasized that the criteria of efficiency to be applied to memory organizations are not the same, for nature is able to "grow" vast parallel systems, concurrently, by just providing the right conditions and milieu. Defective natural components drop out of the system automatically by chancing to be incapable of surviving in competition with effective components, whereas in man-made machines every elementary component must be individually formed, selected, tested, and assembled into the system, modern film-chip manufacturing techniques not withstanding. Again, there is no evidence that man-made elements wear out through use, and can be expected to last just about as long, on the average, if operated so as to change state ten million times per second as when they sit statically in one state or the other. Despite these differences between the elements that are man made and the elementary cells (to the extent that they are known) that nature uses in constructing memories, it seems a very great, if not impossible, jump to try and go from an understanding of the elementary cell to the strict deduction of memory organization logically implied by the cell unit. No attempt will be made here to do this.

However, it is of interest to reflect that certain characteristics of computer memory organization that might be taken for granted as essential to any memory, appear not to be typical of biological memory systems. For example, the prevalence of explicit addressing systems within computer organizations necessitates expressing all problems to the machine in terms of locations within the machine, and this corresponds to an "empty cell" state diagram of the machine. Also it provides, as a byproduct, the ability to command the machine to empty itself and restore itself to some initial state, regardless of what computation is in it at the time. Thus the machine is reversible with respect to any "en route" calculating state or, as algebraists might express it, every elementary calculating state of the machine has a unique inverse operation, by means of which it can be put back into the zero (cleared) state. For a general purpose computer to be used over and over again, this is necessary. Without it certain calculations, once started, might not effectively be reversible by manipulating the input terminals, even if their entire genesis were known.

On the other hand, in biological memory systems, there seems good evidence that no explicit independent addressing system is present. Although the evidence is, in the last resort, introspective and indirect concerning biological systems, it seems strongly to indicate that there exists no operation corresponding to "go to memory address XYZ and clear it to zero (empty) state." In fact, once a human has received a piece of information and stored it "securely"* in memory, the evidence seems to point clearly to the conclusion that whatever it is that gets stored cannot be erased deliberately by the subject or by any other person who may be attempting to construct an inverse operation applicable to the normal input channels of the human "calculating" system. Thus memory of a regretted act lingers on forever and can be denied or reinterpreted in some other (perhaps more acceptable) framework but cannot be expunged from the record.

The irreversible or unerasable property of human memory systems, for which there is considerable evidence derived from hypnosis, use of drugs (etc.) has been offered as the key argument that human memory systems do not use explicit independent addressing. This leads to another postulate about how items are accessed in human memories, and this is by sending a replica (in the same representation code as originally used) again into the memory via the normal input channels. If this is indeed a correct description of the sole method of recalling anything whatever from human memory, then this postulate is sufficient to explain the absence of an erasure capability, for no input statement to the system would be possible concerning any item, without explicitly including that item in the message, and therefore the re-input of the item redeposits it in memory storage.

---

* This term will be explicated below.

It is clear that, however it is organized, the human memory must be a very complex system, having many stages of process depth between which there must exist monitoring and "filtering" discriminators, which act so as to interpret and re-code whatever is on their input and to selectively pass on these interpretations to deeper stages of the storage system. Since interpretation and recoding operations can be visualized as projections of the new input messages against a framework of past accepted interpretations, it is clear that each new input set can be encoded so as to be adjoined to that which has been coded and stored in the past and that the coding can thereby be made efficient and compact.* Clearly the outer layer stages of this successive encoding can be accomplished primarily with "temporary" memory facilities and a modest number of decoding criteria serving to eliminate most of the input messages as "not significant." For example, in proceeding down a gravel walk with eyes downcast, it can easily be shown that a few miles of complete visual detail might saturate any conceivable human memory capacity, so that it is clear that the only message passing beyond the early discriminator stages is simply "gravel walk" suitably encoded. Prevalent theories of human memory include the postulate that selection of pathways through the multi-layered discriminator system is accomplished by a routing method describable as "wearing down pathways" by repetitive use. Whether this postulate is consistent with what is known about human memory behavior is open to question but it is certainly suggestive and convenient. The only point essential to the present discussion is the postulate that the human memory system does have successive stages of interpretation, and that only the inner stages represent permanently irreversible memory storage functions. Thus the outer stages can be compared in function to computer scratch pad memories, with much deliberate rejection of detailed data (like computational round-off) before it ever gets stored, and which are provided with small numbers of discriminatory criteria or "sorting constants" fed forward from the inner stages and updated periodically.

It may be of interest to make a brief excursion into some of the knowledge—and belief—that is available to characterize some aspects of the human memory system. Some twenty years ago, estimates

---

* In essence, each new item can be expressed as some set of old items plus a few new descriptors, so that the "words" of the stored messages grow.

of the number of nerve cells present in the human cortex made by cytologists ranged between 10^9 and 10^{10}, with the number of synapses (critical connections) being in the range of a few to a few dozen. Today estimates of the number of cells tend to be 10^{10} or more and, what is more important, the number of synapses is estimated by electron microscopy to be often in the range of 10^4 or more. These numbers are so enormous that they are almost of no use in guessing at how the memory of the brain can be organized; they are great enough to provide for almost any imaginable scheme. With regard to reliability of functions of the organ, it has often been questioned how such an enormous number of elements can avoid making errors quite frequently. Of course, one answer is that the in-out data rate of the system is rather low so that individual errors in the stored population would be a long time between disclosures. Also, that because the in-out data rate is low, much "checking" of each message by the monitoring discriminators or filters can be accomplished with respect to "criteria of reasonableness" before disclosure. But an even more conclusive answer has often been pointed out, namely that, by storing multiple copies of each item, the chances of failure can be reduced to insignificant levels. This has been most clearly indicated by Minsky[6] who takes the example of each message being stored in n places at random, in which case, removal of one-half the brain would remove one-quarter of the records if $n = 2$, one-eighth of the records if $n = 3$, and $1/2^n$ of the records for any n. If the duplication number n were tenfold, damage to the brain, sufficiently moderate to allow the subject to survive, would probably not be discernible by any externally applicable test. In addition, there is some reason to believe that the apparent permanent difficulties in recall after damage, surgery, etc. are probably due to interference with the recall pathways rather than simply to the loss of stored data.

A great mass of interesting (though highly subjective) data exists with regard to memory disabilities of various sorts, including cortical tissue damage and removal by accident, surgery and disease. Clearly there are many types of difficulties involved in the interpretations of any such data, but the problem of what kinds of side effects are likely to be associated with such damage are such as to discourage treating the reports as suitable for any scientific purpose beyond scientific curiosity and speculation. For example, to turn Minsky's argument around and use it another way, if the cortical memory system were so organized that each item were stored in ten places, but the access pathways to and from each of ten arbitrary sub-sections of the brain were guaranteed to pass through several other such sub-sections, then the probability of interfering with almost everything stored in memory by removing any slice could be made arbitrarily high. It can be said simply that we do not know enough facts at present to permit secure interpretations.

However, there is one type of information regarding malfunction of the human memory system that seems just a little bit less dubious than data involving removal of cortical tissue, and these are data supplied by Russell[9] on recovery of memory after concussions. He reports that, characteristically, memory recovery begins with clear recall for early events, and only gradually advances in time toward events just prior to the accident. As memory recovers, essentially everything up to a given time is very clear to the subject, and with each time advance the memory recovery for that period is almost immediately substantially as complete as ever. Occasionally, memory recovery is in time intervals, with complete amnesia outside the limits of the interval and complete recall within.

This type of observation concerning the gross behavior of the human memory system is so explicit and intriguing that the temptation to erect a card house of speculative ideas upon it is irresistible. Consider a memory system without explicit addressing features, operating in a mode where each item of data (input experience) would constitute its own description, and would proceed, so to speak, as far into the system as required to find a place to be stored. It could be forwarded in parallel along many candidate pathways, passing discriminatory stations at which it would be required to undergo a test match as it penetrated inward to central areas. At each boundary of a test-layer it would try for a match on each pathway, and if the match were perfect at any pathway, the result would be to "add one in some way" to a counter residing there, and the message terminated in all pathways at that layer. If the match were incomplete, a different tally count would be added at the site of the matching part, and the difference forwarded. Eventually the difference would either be eliminated by match-subtraction and then all forwarding would cease, or some part of the advancing item would emerge into new territory and be stored.

The overall behavior of such a storage organization would be that the access pathways of the memory system would be built up sequentially, not with regard to absolute time but as an historic sequence peculiar to the individual who experienced that particular sequence of events. Two people would access their memories by different pathway systems depending on their individual experiences, and in different order of comparison with regard to any new "test input." All persons would recall by sending test-messages down sequential pathways of which the early events would be those of the subject's early personal experience. In all cases early experience would be reinforced continually. For every "match," signals are sent to the "decision" areas of the logical system, so that reinforcing due to recycling (etc.) could be provided. Of course, the standard difficulty with such models is their problem of getting started or choosing initial conditions under which the resulting process would prove neither too restrictive nor too ramified.

The foregoing discussion has been concerned with *theories* of memory. It has not emphasized either the experimental techniques or mathematical techniques necessary to lay a foundation for research in this area, nor to gauge confidence in the prospects for successful effort along these lines. An appreciation of the importance of such technical tools is absolutely vital if these interesting ideas are to advance beyond the point of curiosity; one must be prepared to calculate and estimate simple examples in order to gauge complex situations. These serve the same purpose as simple examples of 2×2 or 3×3 matrices having integer elements serve in the study of abstract group theory; they illustrate the process and connect the theory with something more down-to-earth.

It is hoped that the discussion has provoked interest in the many problems related to theories of memory.

BIBLIOGRAPHY

[1] Aoki, M. and Estrin, G., "The Fixed-Plus-Variable Computer System in Dynamic Programming Formulation of Control System Optimization Problems—Part I," *Report No. 60-66,* UCLA, May, 1961.

[2] Fuller, R. H., "Content Addressible Memory Systems," *Report No. 63-65,* UCLA, June, 1963.

[3] Hebb, D. O., *The Organization of Behavior,* John Wiley and Sons, Inc., New York, N. Y., 1949.

[4] Holland, J., "A Universal Computer Capable of Executing an Arbitrary Number of Subprograms Simultaneously," *Proc. Eastern Joint Computer Conference,* Dec. 1959, p. 108-113.

[5] Karp, R. M. and Mitler, R. E., "Properties of a Model for Parallel Computations: Determinacy, Termination, Queuing" *IBM Watson Research Center RC 1285,* Sept. 1964.

[6] Minsky, M. L., *Proc. 22nd International Congress, Physiological Sciences,* "Information Processing in the Nervous System," p. 302-309.

[7] Newell, A. and Simon, H. A., "The Logic Theory Machine," *IRE Transactions on Information Theory IT-2,* p. 61-79, Sept. 1956.

[8] Rajchman, J. A., "Integrated Magnetic and Superconductive Memories" *Proc. NAS 52* No. 2, p. 363-371, Aug. 1964. See also references contained therein.

[9] Russell, William R., *Brain, Memory and Learning,* Oxford, 1959.

[10] Slade, A. E. and Smallman, C. R., "Thin Film Cryotron Catalogue Addressible Memory," *Automatic Control,* p. 46-50, Aug. 1960.

[11] Slotnick, D. L., Borck, W. C., McReynolds, R. C., "The Solomon Computer," *Proc. Fall Joint Computer Conference,* Philadelphia, Dec. 1962.

[12] Kiseda, J. R., Petersen, H. E., Seeback, W. C. and Teig, M., "A Magnetic Associative Memory," IBM *General Research and Development,* Vol. 5, p. 106-121, April 1961.

VIII. Biological Clocks[1]

The Functions, Ancient and Modern, of Circadian Oscillations

COLIN S. PITTENDRIGH

DE MAIRAN'S PHENOMENON

ERWIN BÜNNING has drawn attention to a remarkable, brief note by the French geologist, De Mairan, written in 1729. De Mairan was evidently intrigued by the daily movements, up and down, of the leaves of certain plants. Hoping to elucidate the nature of their environmental causes he took one of these plants, *Mimosa,* into a cave where it was free of any daily cycle of light or temperature. To his surprise De Mairan found the daily periodicity of movement persisted in this essentially aperiodic environment. Recognizing the importance of his discovery De Mairan commended the problem to his botanical colleagues. In his closing comments he anticipated slow progress in the matter—not, to be sure, because he held a low opinion of botanists but, he says, because progress in science is wholly dependent on experiment and he presumably foresaw no obvious experimental attack on his surprising discovery.

De Mairan's phenomenon attracted a long and distinguished line

---

1. This paper is necessarily a brief condensation of the material covered in nearly four hours of lecture and discussion. The condensation has not treated all sections of the oral presentation equally; the mechanism of entrainment of circadian rhythms by light and the bearing of that mechanism on the problem of photoperiodic time-measurements was discussed at length. It is omitted here. In attempting to give a short written paper some focus I have elected to develop some speculations that were raised only in discussion during the Cloudcroft Seminar.

COLIN S. PITTENDRIGH is Professor of Zoology at Princeton University and, in July 1965, was named Dean of the Princeton Graduate School. He is an AFOSR grantee and a member of the Scientific Advisory Group for the Office of Aerospace Research. He is on the Space Sciences Board of the National Academy of Sciences and of the Biological Sciences Committee of the National Aeronautics and Space Administration.

of botanists in the 19th Century including De Candolle, Hofmeister, Sachs, Darwin and, especially, Wilhelm Pfeffer. Pfeffer is, of course, far better known for his discovery of osmosis and many other contributions to plant physiology than he is for two books, one in 1875 and the other in 1915, on the persistent daily rhythmicity of leaf movements.

To Sachs in the late 1800's it was already clear that the light cycle of the environment was not forcing any periodicity on the plant, it was only serving to control the timing of a periodicity arising internally from other causes. All of the botanists at the end of the 19th Century were concerned to some extent with what adaptive functions these oscillations served. It was not obvious that any useful purpose was involved at all. Darwin, not surprisingly, was nevertheless confident that some purpose had to exist, the implication being, of course, that to evolve as a result of natural selection some adaptive advantage is necessary.

The Endogenous (vs. Exogenous) Origin of the Oscillations

A major theme running through the literature at the turn of the century—and continuing up to 1930—was the possibility that the rhythmicity persisting in constant darkness and constant temperature arose from forces external to the plant; that some unknown Factor-X, an unidentified periodicity in the physical environment, was forcing the rhythmicity. Even today there is still, in fact, one laboratory that remains convinced of the reality of Factor-X. Professor Frank A. Brown, Jr. of Northwestern University has published a long series of studies in which he claims to detect precise 24-hour periodicities in various organic activities (respiration, movements, etc.) that remain phase-fixed to local time. These periodicities (whose reality has been questioned on statistical grounds) he attributes to control by Factor-X. His position has, however, met with considerable criticism in the field. The great majority of workers has long since concluded that De Mairans' phenomenon arises from wholly endogenous, not exogenous, causes.

The evidence for this view derives from various kinds of observation. The principal ones are as follows: The periodicity persisting in constant dark and constant temperature can be stopped by anoxia or low temperature and resumes when oxygen is returned to the system or the temperature is raised again to a level at which metabolism can proceed. The energy on which the oscillation depends is of metabolic origin. When it resumes, after anoxia or low temperature treatment, it does so at essentially the point where it stopped. Implicit in this statement is the important fact, demonstrable with many other techniques, that the phase of the rhythm in constant darkness is wholly independent of local time—that is, of the phase of the earth's rotation and hence of all factors (including the unknown Factor-X) dependent on the earth's rotation.

The most impressive fact in this context is that in organisms in which it can be measured precisely, the period of the rhythm persisting in darkness is not precisely that of the earth's rotation (Figure 1). Proponents of the endogenous nature of these rhythms (including the writer) argue that only by adducing the most cumbersome and unlikely additional assumptions can one explain the origin of, say, a 23 hour and 15 minute period as the product of an (unknown) driving cycle with a period of precisely 24 hours. Franz Halberg has introduced the term circadian (L. *circa, dies*) for De Mairan's oscillations. This term emphasizes the theoretically important discrepancy between their period and that of the earth's rotation. It also obviates the conflict of meanings inherent in diurnal (vs. nocturnal) which has often been used. The phrase "daily rhythms" lacks the precision and implication of Halberg's "circadian rhythm."

Individuals within a species differ, genetically, in their free-running periods—that is, in the period they manifest when uncontrolled by an environmental light cycle. And their periods are also open to some experimental manipulation principally as a result of prior light treatments.

As a matter of fact, it is now unfair to associate Professor Brown with earlier students of Factor-X; he no longer regards Factor-X as the total explanation of De Mairan's phenomenon. He recognizes that the data demand the existence of a periodicity of endogenous origin; his interest in Factor-X focuses on its potential role as a kind of pace-maker that confers precision and temperature compensation on the endogenous oscillation.

THE UBIQUITY AND PERVASIVENESS OF CIRCADIAN OSCILLATIONS

De Mairan's phenomenon has been, by now, observed in a remarkably broad array of organisms: unicellulars, green plants, and animals at all levels of complexity including man himself. It is a general feature of the physiological organization of living things on this planet. This ubiquity is matched by the diversity of functions within the individual organism that manifest the oscillation. In the unicel-

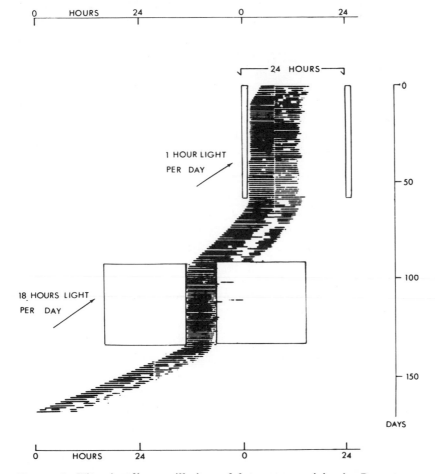

FIGURE 1. The circadian oscillation of locomotry activity in *Peromyscus maniculatus,* freerunning and entrained. A 1:23 light-dark cycle is imposed from day 0 to day 59. The oscillation is captured into entrainment by day 6. From day 60 to day 92 the rhythm again freeruns in constant darkness. An 18:6 light-dark cycle is imposed from day 93 to day 132 when the rhythm is again allowed to free run. Note the remarkable precision of the period of the freerunning oscillation.

lular *Gonyaulax,* Hastings and Sweeney have found circadian oscillations in two distinct aspects of its luminescent system, in photosynthesis and in cell division; in mice or rats virtually every parameter studied is involved—blood chemistry, liver chemistry, cell divisions, body temperature, susceptibility to X-rays and drugs, and so on. The practical importance of these more recent discoveries in mammals is obvious and immense. A given dose of *E. Coli* endotoxin will kill 85% of mice treated at one point in their circadian cycle but only 5% at another (Halberg). Similarly extreme effects have been reported, again by Halberg, for the drug ouabain. Gertrude Stein to the contrary notwithstanding, a rose is not necessarily and unqualifiedly a rose; that is to say, it is a very different biochemical system at noon and at midnight. The phase of the organism's circadian cycle of change is a parameter of major importance the physiologist cannot ignore. Nor can the pharmacologist!

We have found, paralleling Halberg's observations, that the behavior to a fixed stimulus and the temperature tolerance of *Drosophila,* is markedly different at different circadian phases. And along with many other laboratories we have found significant differences in the specific activity of a given enzyme system assayed in vitro after extraction in the middle of the subjective day and the middle of the subjective night. In our (Uwo, Nakajima, Townsend and Pittendrigh, *in press*) case we found differences in the Michaelis Constant for the system, day and night.

THE PRECISION, INNATENESS AND TEMPERATURE COMPENSATION OF CIRCADIAN OSCILLATIONS

For ease of assay circadian rhythmicity is most conveniently studied by recording some behavioral feature of the whole organism. In mammals, for instance (Figure 1), locomotion lends itself to a very useful assay. Rodents have a curious predilection for exercise on running wheels. The time at which they begin and continue this activity is easily recorded by coupling the running wheel via a microswitch to an operations recorder. Every time the wheel is rotated a pen mark is made on the horizontal lines (24 hour length) in e.g. Figure 1. The onset of their activity in 24 hour cycles of light and dark is precise; in nocturnal species it begins at or near "sunset." When the organism is put into De Mairan's conditions of constant darkness and temperature, the periodicity persists with remarkably clear definition and persists indefinitely. The period of the rhythm, as measured by the intervals between activity onsets, is circadian.

The precision and indefinite persistence of the rhythmicity are among its most striking features. The standard error of the period in some of these free-running rodents may be no more than about a minute. In other words the "error" is of the order 1 in 1000.

The rhythmicity is, moreover, innate to the organism; it is not learned by prior experience (in the individual) of a daily periodicity in the environment. Rigorous demonstrations of innateness have been made in unicellulars, insects and vertebrates.

Perhaps the most surprising property of circadian oscillations is the fact that their period changes only very slightly with considerable changes in temperature. This temperature-compensation of the oscillation is a large topic in its own right. It has played a major role in F. A. Brown's thinking. The difficulty of giving a simple physiological explanation for it led him, in part, to his renewed concern with the possible existence and function of an external physical pacemaker (Factor-X). On the other hand, it was a property this writer inferred should be general if circadian oscillations were fulfilling a general clock-function—a topic to which I shall return shortly.

THE CELLULAR BASIS OF CIRCADIAN OSCILLATIONS

A significant result in the last ten years has been the demonstration that De Mairan's rhythms do not depend on the greater complexity of multicellular organization. Single cells manifest the rhythm—in, for example, *Euglena, Gonyaulax, Paramecium* and the alga *Acetabularia*. Sonneborn and Barnett have studied a remarkable case in *Paramecium multimicronucleatum*. "Animals" of this species oscillate from one mating type to another in the course of a single day. From what is known of the genetics of mating type in other species this result is suggestive that a single gene may be undergoing a daily cycle of induction and repression.

Several workers have made attempts—mostly abortive—to strive for further delimitation of the level of organization necessary to sustain a circadian oscillation. In particular the question of whether or not the nucleus or cytoplasm is the site of the driving oscillation has been raised.

Sweeney and Haxo (1961) and Richter (1963) have made some

remarkable observations on the famous unicellular alga *Acetabularia* which lends itself readily to such tasks. The localization of the nucleus in one part of a single cell that withstands surgical treatment permits one to ask whether or not the enucleated cytoplasm can sustain a circadian oscillation—in this case, of photosynthetic activity. It can, even for as many as 30 cycles. The ease with which subcellular grafting can be achieved in this alga permitted Schweiger, *et al* (1964) to show, however, that in a "synthetic" cell consisting of nucleus and cytoplasm placed 180° out of phase, the resultant steady state rhythm of the cell is that dictated by the nucleus. In any case the large amounts of DNA in the extranuclear organization of *Acetabularia* render the capacity of its "cytoplasm" to sustain an oscillation of doubtful general significance.

Many attempts have been made to manipulate circadian rhythmicity chemically; and for the most part these attempts have been singularly unsuccessful. In the absence of labeling the negative results are not too significant; there is no assurance the agents applied entered the cells in significant amounts. But at least some of those who have attempted the work are impressed with its apparent insusceptibility to chemical control. There are, to be sure, some reports of positive effects but they are not all fully convincing. Hastings appears to have affected phase shifts in *Gonyaulax* with cyanide arsenite and p-chloromercuribenzoate. Bunning has reported data on the effects of colchicine, urethane and alcohol on period length. And Bruce and Pittendrigh found effects of D_2O on both the phase and period of the *Euglena* system. In any case none of these results has proved fruitful of suggestions as to the chemical basis (if any) of the oscillation.

One of the best known studies along these lines is that of Karakashian and Hastings. Using the unicellular (dinoflagellate) *Gonyaulax* they measured the effects of several antimetabolites known to affect various steps in the protein synthetic mechanism. The action of actinomycin-D is known to affect the production of messenger RNA—the primary step in the transcription of the inherited message of the cell's DNA. They found, following actinomycin treatment, that the rhythms of luminescense and photosynthesis decayed. This result, surely of considerable interest, is however somewhat equivocal as to meaning. The loss of rhythmicity, as such, by no means demonstrates that the agent responsible has affected the cell's clock; its target could as well be the coupling of the clock (or driving oscillation) to the physiological system assayed.

The only unequivocal demonstrations of manipulation of the clock concern either the period of the phase or a steady-state rhythm.

Strumwasser has very recently given evidence on the action of actinomycin that promises to fulfill these requirements. In a brilliant study of circadian rhythmicity in a single ganglion cell from the mollusk *Aplysia,* he has succeeded in making intracellular injections of various agents. The results so far published show a clear phase-shift of the oscillation following injection of actinomycin. At present technical limitations preclude measurement of the rhythm for much more than a single cycle after treatment. We cannot, therefore, be sure that the phase-shift seen in that cycle would persist in the steady-state and thus demonstrate fully that the driving oscillation has been affected and not (again) some coupling mechanism between the driver and the assayed rhythm.

Other suggestions that the nucleic acid systems in the cell are intimately involved in circadian rhythmicity arise from observations by Ehret and, independently, by Sweeney that ultraviolet at 254 mμ can effect steady state phase-shifts. There are pecularities in both Ehret's (*Paramecium*) and Sweeney's (*Gonyaulax*) results that indicate the UV is achieving its effects by a quite distinct route from that of visible radiation.

The Cell and Organism as an Oscillator Entrainable by Light Cycles

In 1957 Bruce and I pointed out that, formally, circadian rhythms are self-sustaining oscillations, and pursued a general comparison between the organism-environment relation and that of two oscillations, one entraining the other. In historical perspective, it is clear that circadian oscillations in the cell and organism are an evolved match to the striking oscillations of the physical environment. Metabolism has evolved an oscillatory time course, and in nature that oscillation in metabolism and behavior assumes a definite phase-relation to the external cycle of physical change. Attainment of that "proper" phase relation is effected—at least principally—by the light cycle. The cellular oscillation couples to the light cycle and is entrained or driven by it. The light cycle, as Sachs long ago recognized, is not *imposing* the rhythm. Its action is strictly comparable, mathematically, to the action of one oscillation entraining another, fully-autonomous, self-sustaining oscillator.

Entrainment implies control in two respects. The entrained oscillation assumes the period (or frequency) of the entraining cycle; when, as in the biological case, the entraining cycle is error-free, the error inherent in the entrained oscillation's imperfections are removed. Second, the entrained oscillation assumes a determinate phase-relation to the entraining cycle. The net biological result is clear temporal control; specific events in the circadian cycle occur at particular times in the environmental cycle.

It is, for the most part, an act of biological faith when we go further and say that the end result is execution of given functions at the "right time of day." This is to follow Darwin in his confidence that some adaptive function does, ultimately, attach to such a remarkable piece of organization. To suppose otherwise is, implicitly, to appeal to something other than natural selection as the historical agent of the system.

I will not, in this written version of my contribution, pursue what is now known of the mechanism of entrainment by light. Suffice it to note a few points of general interest. First, light cycles are universally effective in entraining circadian oscillations. In poikilothermous ("cold-blooded") organisms temperature cycles can also entrain but they are probably always less powerful agents, and recent work by Mr. Zimmerman in our laboratory shows this is certainly the case in *Drosophila*. Second, observations by Halberg, Richter and my laboratory have shown that in mammals the light, in its entraining function, is transduced by the eye; blinded mice, rats and hamsters fail to entrain to light cycles. It is, however, likely that this route is historically secondary. If, as is surely true, the hypothalamus acts as driving center in the system of circadian oscillations within a vertebrate, its coupling to the environmental light cycle will almost necessarily demand an intermediate coupling to a superficial photoreceptor. (It is noted, however, that Ganong's remarkable demonstration of the penetration of the visible into the vertebrate brain stem takes some force from this argument). However, it is equally clear, as experimental fact, that the *Drosophila* circadian system can be entrained without any organized photoreceptor in the larval stage. And several workers (including Lees and

Williams) have demonstrated that photoperiodic induction (which, I shall argue later, is a function of the circadian oscillation) can be effected by the action of light absorbed directly by central nervous tissue. In Paramecium, other unicellulars, and in green plants, the question of an organized "eye" does not arise. They, too, are entrainable by light. The general conclusion is that some molecule in the cell, not specifically devoted to photoreception in the usual visual sense, absorbs the entraining light and is intimately connected with the driving mechanism of the circadian oscillation.

The third point I wish to emphasize about light cycles as entraining agents for circadian oscillations is the general result that the photoperiod in each cycle—the fraction of the period occupied by light—has a major effect on the phase and the waveform (insofar as one can measure or infer this) of the entrained rhythm.

CHROMOMETRY BY CIRCADIAN OSCILLATIONS: CELESTIAL ORIENTATION AND PHOTOPERIODISM

Bruce and I have suggested that the resurge of interest in circadian rhythms since 1950 largely derives from the remarkable studies by Gustav Kramer and Karl von Frisch which showed that birds and bees, respectively, can maintain a given direction throughout the day using the sun as compass. They compensate for the movement of their celestial direction-giver with the aid of an internal 24 hour clock. The experiments supporting these remarkable conclusions are classics of experimental zoology. Hoffman and others have shown that the animals' clock is phased to local time by virtue of being coupled to the environmental light cycle. In starlings Hoffman has shown further that the clock will continue to operate in continuous dim light and proves to be—in these freerunning conditions—a circadian oscillation. Its freerunning period is about $23\frac{1}{2}$ hours.

Kramer's initial demonstration prompted my own reinvestigation of the temperature-relations of the circadian system in *Drosophila*. On the hypothesis—then—that circadian oscillations were the evolutionary foundation of Kramer's clock, it seemed to me that to be useful in this respect they should be temperature compensated; and they proved to be so. Since then (1954) temperature compensation has been shown to be a universal feature of circadian oscillations even in single cells (Bruce and Pittendrigh, 1956). And since 1950 time-compensated sun-orientation has been discovered in a remarkably diverse array of metazoa.

It is clear, however, that this spectacular clock function is recent in the history of life; it has exploited already existing circadian oscillations; it does not account for their initial evolution.

Nearly 15 years before the work of Kramer and von Frisch, Erwin Bünning had related circadian rhythms to a quite distinct set of phenomena—those of photoperiodism. Garner and Allard showed, in 1920, that the switch from vegetative to floral growth in some plants was controlled by the number of hours of daylight—the photoperiod —in each daily cycle. Bünning's suggestion in 1936 was that the endogenous "daily" rhythmicity of plants was causally related to this control. He envisaged what we now call the plant's circadian rhythm as consisting of two half-cycles—one photophilic and the other scotophilic. The latter, in its usual phase relation to the environmental day, lies in the nightly dark period. He suggested that as the length of day changed the early scotophil would be illuminated or not, according to season. When illuminated in long day plants the switch to floral initiation was closed; in short day plants illumination of the early scotophil kept the switch open. His hypothesis, translated into the current jargon, was, in fact, that the circadian oscillation of the plant was serving as the clock that effects the time-measurement implicit in photoperiodism; it was the clock measuring the duration of the daily photoperiod.

That hypothesis was a brilliant stroke in its day. It anticipated the current emphasis on the time-measurement as such as the knottiest problem in photoperiodism, and it anticipated the current treatment of circadian oscillations as biological clocks in general. Yet the hypothesis has met with stubborn opposition by students of both plant and animal photoperiodism. That opposition is now weakening and the evidence today leaves essentially no doubt that Bünning's basic proposition is fundamentally correct (cf. e.g. Pittendrigh and Minis, 1964 and Pittendrigh, 1965).

On the Ancient, or Primary, Function of Circadian Oscillations

Time compensated sun orientation is surely a recent development in the history of organisms. And it seems likely that classical photoperiodism is of more recent origin than circadian oscillations in general. Bünning (1957) has, to be sure, suggested that their role in photoperiodism is their primitive function—the source of the original selection pressures that generated them. That seems, however, very unlikely to this writer. Circadian oscillations are widespread in unicellulars for instance, in which with one recent exception (Steele, 1965) there is no evidence of seasonal control by photoperiod. Bünning's attempt to find functional significance for them in photoperiodism re-emphasizes a point already noted. Since Darwin's day botanists have been hard-pressed to find adaptive meaning for the particular manifestation of circadian rhythmicity they most often encounter and study, viz: the "sleep" movements of leaves. I acknowledged earlier in this paper that the proposition of a "right-time of day" for a given metabolic function is in large part an act of faith. The fact is that, for many of the circadian rhythms selected as obvious and easily assayed, there is no very well defined adaptive function. Remmert (1962) has justifiably questioned—as at least not proven—the adaptive utility I suggested some years ago (1954, 1958) for the *Drosophila* eclosion rhythm. Indeed, Remmert is perplexed about the adaptive function of the huge number of other insect "Schluprythmuen."

The sheer diversity of activities in organisms that manifest circadian rhythms raises a clear question. Are they of independent evolutionary origin or have a common historical origin? Of course, there is no doubt that many of the details of diverse circadian systems are of independent origin, and that some of their formal properties owe their similarity to convergence. It is difficult, however, to accept a convergence from independent origins as the explanation of *all* the similarities they show, especially those most "improbable" physiological features: (1) precision, (2) temperature compensation. They are all similar, too, in their entrainability by light. It is difficult, in short, not to retain as a working position the view that there is common core to the structure of circadian oscillations that is ancient; that they evolved in service of a function not yet explicitly recognized; and the few clearly defined functions they serve today are secondary exploitations of an organization that arose to meet other immediate problems.

If such an ancient, primary function indeed exists, it is certainly not known and the discussion could well rest there. I believe, however, that recognition of the issue is itself important. Functional analysis and explanation is not the only nor even the main task of the biologist; but even when he is primarily concerned, as I am, with physiological explanation, he cannot afford to neglect functional issues as touchstones to progress. Living organization is the product of an historical development molded by natural selection whose only concern is in fact functional. It is then possible that by recognizing the possibility of a primary function, so far not recognized, we may be led to useful new avenues of question and casual analysis.

THE LIGHT CYCLE AS THE PRIMARY AGENT OF SELECTION

The relation of the light cycle to circadian rhythmicity is today recognized only as that of its entraining agent, but it is a reasonable speculation that the daily alternation of light and darkness was the historical cause (selective agent) of circadian oscillations in the first place.

This line of thought derives from recalling the prerequisites for organization in a chemical system. The principal of these is that the constituent reactions cannot proceed spontaneously at the prevailing levels of free energy. Thermochemically this means, of course, that the reactions the cell employs involve energy barriers unsurmountable at prevailing temperatures; they proceed only on command which rests with enzymes and ultimately with the nuclear store of information. Little attention seems to have been given—in this general context—to the problem of visible radiation as an energy source that threatens organization.

Of course, the fact is that the majority of the cell's constituents are colorless; and uncontrolled activation by the visible is thus excluded. It may well be that in the history of the cell there has been selection for colorless molecules, but if that is true (and it seems likely) it is a fact that for some functions colorless molecular devices have not been found. The flavins and cytochromes are examples of ubiquitous fundamentally important molecules that are colored—and where color has no detected function.

No attention seems to have been given to the consequences of illuminating those molecules whose color is without obvious function. At any rate it is surely reasonable to consider, at least, the likelihood that some subroutines in the cell's overall tasks are impaired by the activation of molecular piece-parts in the flood of visible radiation to which it is subjected each day. To that extent the routine delegation of some chemical activity to the recurrent darkness of each night would be an obvious escape from the photochemical threat to organization.

A miscellany of otherwise disconnected facts has suggested to me that we should not ignore this line of thought and further that the activities involved may concern the cell's central controls—those of protein synthesis and specification. I noted earlier that there is suggestive but not yet compelling evidence from actinomycin and UV treatments that the nucleic acids are intimately involved in the cell's driving oscillation. There is, too, the long known fact that an enzyme system involved in repairing UV damage to the genetic material absorbs in the visible; this is the phenomenon of photoreactivation. The enzyme concerned is incidentally evidently involved in the mechanism of genetic recombination—at least in bacteria. And the miscellany is completed by the observation of Sulkowski, Slonimski and colleagues that gene induction (in yeast) can be inhibited, at least for some hours, by visible radiation during the transition from anaerobic to aerobic metabolism. It is certain, at least, that part, and perhaps an important part, of the central control mechanism absorbs the visible and is functionally significantly affected by the resulting activation. The possibility arises that one way of coping with this activation is to restrict the steps concerned—perhaps gene induction itself—to the daily dark period.

CIRCADIAN OSCILLATIONS AS SYNCHRONIZING GATES IN THE TIMING OF DEVELOPMENTAL STEPS

I noted some years ago (1954) that the circadian rhythm in *Drosophila pseudoobscura* was functioning as a synchronizing gate for the act of eclosion. In spite of Harker's (1965) recent discussions, this remains clearly true. But recent work by Skopik and me at Princeton demonstrates that the synchronization manifest at eclosion must occur much earlier in pupal development. Harker's data, which she interprets radically differently, show, in our view, the same result. When a circadian oscillation is initiated in *Drosophila* at any stage in its development, the remainder of development takes a time to completion that is strictly *modulo* the period of the oscillation.

We are currently concerned with the implication that the initiations of new subroutines in development are gated by the circadian oscillation in the system in a manner broadly comparable to that of a master clock in a synchronous computer. In such computers the inputs necessary from a diversity of subroutines—some slow, some fast—are guaranteed to be available by postponing the initiation of the next round until a gate is opened; and that gate, timed by a master clock, occurs with a frequency adjusted to the slowest subroutines. Synchronous computers are, thus, slower than the more elaborate asychronous devices that can be built, but they are cheaper. All real computers involve a mix of asynchronous and synchronous features. And it is obvious that the organized reading and execution of the cell's DNA is not always regulated by synchronous gates—and certainly not by gates recurring with a period as long as 24 hours. But it is by no means excluded that selection has seized the opportunity of circadian oscillations, especially if they involve a reading of the message, to buy a degree of organization more cheaply than is otherwise possible. There is an obvious appeal in the idea of a temperature-compensated oscillation functioning as a synchronous gating device in a system whose piece-parts are conspicuously temperature dependent. A *Drosophila* egg raised at 10° or 28°C yields a fly that is essentially the same; morphogenesis and differentiation are temperature compensated; the reading of the message is temperature compensated.

It is clear that if, in eukaryotic forms, the cell has restricted some light-sensitive step in message reading to the daily dark period, it has also, *ipso facto,* instituted a temperature-compensated synchronizing gate. What we are now pursuing in *Drosophila* is precisely this idea. The working position is that eclosion is only a special case of a general gating, by the circadian oscillation, of all new gene inductions; inducer may have been available earlier but induction awaits a once daily scan of the message. This view is encouraged for us by Harker's facts which she interprets in a fundamentally different way. She appears almost to deny the existence of oscillations in individual flies and regards the time of eclosion as determined by summing the intervals between earlier developmental steps. It is, of course, trivially true that such summation occurs; eclosion is the end of development. What she ignores is the fact that development times are always n times the period of circadian oscillation and further that her own data indicate that each new step, like the appearance of eye or wing color, tends to be phase-fixed to the light cycle—and hence to the circadian oscillation.

This frankly speculative excursion into the history and primary functional significance of circadian rhythmicity would be unjustified were it not suggestive of new experimental work. Fortunately, it is. We are, in fact, greatly encouraged in testing the proposition that the timing of new morphogenetic events in mid-development is as manipulable by the phase of circadian oscillation (itself manipulable by brief light flashes) as the terminal event of eclosion itself.

It is not difficult to relate this line of thought to the involvement of circadian rhythms in photoperiodic induction. The change in day length that occurs with season effects a switch in metabolic program —as from vegetative to floral growth. That change demands evocation of a part of the nuclear message otherwise ignored or suppressed. In short, photoperiodic induction must, in last analysis, involve induction of specific genes. The prospect that induction is restricted to a daily scan of the message in each dark period is clearly compatible with the further idea that induction of a given gene lying towards the end of the scanning sequence is as photosensitive as the inductions Sulkowski *et al* have observed in yeast cells. There is, of course, evidence now from bacterial studies that any scan of the message—for replication or reading—will begin at a fixed point and proceed linearly down the fixed species specific codon sequence. The meager facts available indicate a scanning time for replication in eukaryotic cells of 6 or 8 hours; it is reasonable to anticipate that a reading scan will take essentially the same time—which is in the right range for measurement of night length.

The scope of the speculation I have ventured here guarantees that much of it will be wrong. Its justification is in part its testability, as I noted. But it is also justified if, in isolating and emphasizing the question of a primary unidentified function for circadian oscillations, the speculation prompts new questions and experiments.

IX. Combustion Instability

Frank T. McClure

THE TOPIC that I have chosen for today is both complex and rather specialized, yet in a sense these very features make it appropriate for this seminar. Much science in the sixties is characterized by attacks on complex problems. This comes about for two reasons. First, because of the development of modern instrumentation in the experimental field and computing machines in the theoretical field, it becomes possible to attack problems of greater complexity. Second, because science and technology have become such a major factor in our society it is necessary to attack complex problems if they are important to technological advance. Those of us who are in the sciences close to the applied areas must, in fact, choose our problems because of their importance rather than for their simplicity. Our approach, therefore, is guided by the need for a solution and limited by our abilities and by the techniques and equipment available to us. Nevertheless, the classical approach is absolutely vital to the handling of complex problems. The steps are, as they have always been, analysis and synthesis—or if you like, resynthesis. By this I mean that the problem must be broken down into its simplest components, and each of those components studied until it is thoroughly understood. The idea is to define simpler, but pertinent, problems within the grasp of one's understanding. Having mastered the details of these simpler problems, one then attempts a synthesis —or resynthesis—to see whether the knowledge of the simpler problems provides an adequate understanding of the whole phenomenon. If it does, then we have success. If it doesn't, then we obviously have

FRANK T. McCLURE is chairman of the Research Center of the Applied Physics Laboratory of the Johns Hopkins University, and a contributor to a variety of fields from the biophysics of the brain to rocket science. In 1961, he won the first National Aeronautics and Space Administration Contributions Award for his conception of a system of navigating ships at sea by the doppler signals from an earth satellite. This led to the Transit and the presently operational Navy Navigation Satellite Systems.

left out some important feature in our analysis, and we must go back to see what it was.

Another feature of science in the sixties is the stress on teamwork. This is also not new, for throughout the history of science workers have built on the efforts of predecessors or contemporaries. Today, however, at the pace at which we demand solution of problems, rapid exchange of information becomes even more essential. Again I think the subject that I will discuss today illustrates this very clearly. The work that I will describe comes from a number of investigators, among whom I should specifically mention Angelus at the Allegany Ballistics Laboratory, Wood at Rohm & Haas, Price and Horton at the Naval Ordnance Test Station, Swithenbank and Sotter at Sheffield University, Levine at Rocketdyne and Ryan at the University of Utah, along with my colleagues Hart, Bird, Cantrell and Foner at The Applied Physics Laboratory. My remarks will depend heavily on the work done by these men within the past five or six years.

Acoustic Instability

There are several kinds of combustion instability. I will limit this lecture to one kind alone, namely, high frequency instability—or as I prefer to call it, acoustic instability. This kind of instability occurs in both liquid and solid rockets. I will devote my detailed discussion to the phenomenon in solid rockets. Many of the things that I say are equally applicable to the problem in liquid rockets. I shall mention a few of the features of liquid rockets at the end.

First, let me remind you of the nature of a solid rocket. It normally appears as a hollow cylinder, the interior walls of which are covered by solid propellant. This solid propellant has a so-called linear burning rate, namely, the rate at which the surface regresses normal to itself as the propellant is consumed. The linear burning rate is dependent upon the pressure in the chamber and upon the gas velocity sweeping across the surface, or, if you like, tangential to the surface. This latter phenomenon, namely the dependence upon the gas velocity across the surface, is called the "erosive" component of burning. The velocity distribution within the rocket motor is dependent upon its geometry, and since the burning away of the solid makes the geometry itself dependent upon the time, the burning rate of the propellant is dependent upon the time. The mass rate of production of gas will depend upon the product of the burning rate and the surface area of the propellant exposed to the gases. To a good approximation, the mass rate of discharge of gas from the rocket through the nozzle is proportional to the pressure within the rocket. A constant pressure within the rocket can then be obtained by tailoring the geometry of the propellant charge so that the variation of surface area exposed to the hot gases will keep the product of the surface area and the burning rate constant at a constant pressure. Since, in general, the erosion will decrease as time goes on because the channels will open as the propellant burns away, this means that the surface must be arranged to be slightly progressive, that is, the surface area increases somewhat with time. For the purpose of this lecture, it suffices to say that there are a number of ways of designing the geometry of propellant charge so that these characteristics can be met. Then one would expect a steady constant pressure as the rocket burns. These rather general considerations fall into the field of steady state interior ballistics. The principles are quite well understood in a semi-empirical sense, and one can go about the design of a rocket on the basis of these principles with some degree of assurance, providing a steady state really exists.

But does the steady state exist? One of the frustrating experiences for the rocket designer comes about because of the failure of this criterion to be met. Having designed a rocket according to the well known principles of steady state interior ballistics, the designer is often horrified to see that his device performs beautifully for a portion of its burning time and then, for some strange reason, blows up. If he then constructs the same rocket motor in a case of thick walled steel —a so-called "battleship" case—he finds that for some time the pressure approximates very closely that which he predicted, then suddenly jumps to a new level considerably higher than the steady state level. Of course, in a light-weight case, the rocket would rupture when this pressure jump occurs.

If he now places within the rocket gauges that respond to very high frequency, he finds that there are oscillations in pressure at say 1000 cycles per second, or 10,000, or perhaps 20,000. Analysis of these frequencies indicates that the natural acoustic modes of the cylinder of gas are excited to very high levels. These acoustic modes of the cylindrical gas column within the rocket may be described as axial or transverse—depending upon the motion of the gas. If the gas motion is back and forth along the axis of the cylinder, then one is dealing with an axial mode. On the other hand, if the gas motion is predominantly in a plane perpendicular to the axis of the cylinder, the mode is transverse. Among the transverse modes are the radials and the tangentials. In the radial modes, the motion of the gas is back and forth along the radii of the cylinder. In the tangentials the motion is predominantly around the circumference of the cylinder. In the first tangential, for example, the gas more or less sloshes back and forth from one side of the cylinder to the other. In the second tangential, the gas sloshes back and forth in pie shaped sectors, with four such sectors to the cross section of the cylinder. In the third tangential, there would be six such pie shaped sectors. The most general mode of the oscillation of the gas in the cylinder is a combination of axial, radial and tangential motions. One or another of these modes or perhaps several at one time may be excited. To make the problem more complicated, it should be remembered that the geometry is changing with time, because the propellant is burning away. Thus the frequency of the modes is changing with time. Therefore, the "music" played by this rocket can be quite complex. The intensity of the "sound" waves observed is quite striking. Their amplitudes can reach several hundred psi in a rocket whose steady state pressure might be 500 psi. These are sound waves outside the normal realm of experience.

To make things more complicated, the solid propellant itself is also an elastic medium. Thus the annular column of solid propellant can itself support stress waves. This becomes important when a natural mode of the propellant corresponds in frequency to a natural mode of the gas. At that point, the solid goes into violent oscillation with considerable loss of energy through visco-elastic forces, and as a result the oscillation is damped.

If we now focus our attention upon the transverse waves, we will note that for a given mode the frequency in the gas phase will fall with time because the diameter of the cylindrical gas column is increasing. On the other hand, the corresponding mode in the solid will rise in frequency with time because the thickness of the solid annulus is decreasing. From time to time a mode excited in the gas will be damped by oscillation in the solid. The system may be stable for awhile and then excited in some other mode or perhaps again in the same mode. The time course of the phenomenon can thus be quite complicated.

THE CAUSE OF EXCESSIVE PRESSURE

Acoustic modes of the system may be excited to high amplitude. But why does the average pressure of the system change so drastically? Either the propellant must have burned more rapidly than expected or the discharge of gas through the nozzle must have occurred less rapidly.

One method of examining this problem is to perform a "partial burning." In this technique a heavy walled motor is caused to rupture at, say, its head end by means of explosive bolts or similar devices, at a predetermined time after the initiation of burning. The consequent sudden drop of pressure extinguishes the burning of the propellant. The remaining propellant may then be examined to see whether excessive burning has occurred. Such experiments indeed show that there has been excessive burning at various places on the propellant surface. These regions of excessive burning are distributed in a complicated way. One source of this excessive burning is called "acoustic erosion." Consider a transverse mode, say the first tangential. The motion of the gas is back and forth across the surface. Now, erosive burning consists of the increase in burning rate due to the flow of gas across a surface. It will not normally be dependent upon the direction of flow across the surface. In our tangential mode, for one half cycle the gas will flow in one direction across the surface and in the second half cycle the flow will be in the other direction. The erosive response, however, will be an increase in burning rate in both half cycles. The increase in burning rate due to erosion in the first half cycle will be added to, rather than compensated for, by the increase in burning rate in the second half cycle. The net result, therefore, is an increase in burning rate at the areas where the velocity maxima in the acoustic wave pattern occur, with little or no compensation elsewhere.

This phenomenon of acoustic erosion suffices in many cases to explain the increase in pressure when the acoustic wave is excited. There are, however, cases in which the total rise in pressure is too high to be explained even qualitatively by acoustic erosion. The explanation is given by another phenomenon characteristic of very high amplitude sound waves. High amplitude sound waves transport fluid. This transport of fluid is called "acoustic streaming." Acoustic streaming in conjunction with the general flow pattern within the rocket motor generates vortices. This was predicted about ten years years ago by Maslen and Moore and observed recently experimentally by Swithenbank and Sotter at the University of Sheffield, England. These vortices cause high surface velocities across the propellant in localized regions. By erosive burning the propellant is scoured out in these areas. This additional erosive burning adds to the excessive burning of the propellant.

In one class of modes still another factor must be considered. In the previous discussion, we implicitly referred to the so-called standing tangentials. Another common and very important mode is the traveling tangential. In this mode, the sound wave runs around and around the cylinder in one direction. The first traveling tangential generates, by acoustic streaming, a central vortex of considerable strength. We not only get excessive erosion due to this vortex but the gas is rotating rapidly and by centrifugal action is thrown to the wall of the nozzle. The effective throat area of the nozzle is thus decreased so that the discharge rate is decreased. Now we have not only an increased burning rate but also a lower discharge rate, and the two combined give a very great increase in operating pressure. As a point which will be discussed later, it should also be mentioned that this traveling tangential wave can be induced by introducing a tangential flow of gas by a jet at the periphery of the motor.

THE SOURCES OF ACOUSTIC ENERGY

We have now discussed how high amplitude sound waves can bring about elevated pressures and destruction of the rocket motor. We have not, however, explained how the high amplitude sound waves come about themselves. To understand this, we must go back to the question of the combustion of the solid propellant. In a very thin layer, generally under 100 microns thick, the chemical energy of the propellant is released as thermal energy contained in the hot product gases. Within this thin region, the solid propellant is heated to a point at which it evolves partially reacted gases from its surface. These gases are warmed to higher temperatures where they finally react to form the very hot product gases. The thickness of this whole zone and the consequent rate of reaction are dependent upon pressure. The question then arises as to how this zone responds to an oscillating pressure. If the zone puffs out new gas in phase with the pressure, then mechanical work will be delivered into the cylinder of gas. The result is that this interaction with the burning propellant will tend to amplify the sound wave. If this amplification tendency of the burning surface overcomes the losses elsewhere in the system, the acoustic wave will, in fact, grow in amplitude, and may reach very high amplitudes before second order effects limit further growth. The appropriate characteristic of the burning surface describing this property is the so called "response function." This is the in-phase component of the fractional mass burning rate per unit area divided by the fractional pressure oscillation. No complete theory of the response function of a burning propellant exists. This is not too surprising because no complete theory of the simpler problem of the steady state burning of solid propellants exists. However, a theory of the response function for an oversimplified model of the burning of a solid propellant has been worked out and it shows that one should expect amplification of sound waves over a very broad frequency band extending from several hundred cycles per second to two or three tens of thousands of cycles per second. Thus, providing the acoustic losses in the system are not too great, one may expect the building up of acoustic modes over this very wide frequency band, and this, indeed is the experience.

In recent years, experimental measurements of response functions have become possible using a technique called the T-burner. In this device, which may be described as a pipe closed at both ends with an opening in the middle to exhaust gases, propellant may be burned at one or both ends in the form of a flat slab covering the end of the pipe. Measurement of the logarithmic growth and decay of oscillations in such a system can lead, with some approximations, to values of the response function of the propellant used. This technique has been highly developed by Price and Horton at the Naval Ordnance Test Station, by Ryan and Coates at the University of Utah and by Watermeier and Strittmater at the Ballistic Research Laboratories at Aberdeen. A somewhat more versatile extension of the technique has been developed by Foner at the Applied Physics Laboratory. In a general sense, the measurements tend to verify the simple theory. The results show the broad banded nature of the frequency response. The scaling of frequency vs. burning rate is similar to that predicted by the oversimplified theory. At low pressures where the burning rate is low, or with propellants with burning rate suppressants to slow the burning, the response functions, while of the right order of magnitude, tend to be larger than one would expect from the simple theory, by perhaps a factor of two. Inclusion of radiation effects—that is the heating of the propellant surface by means of black body radiation transmitted from the hot gases—in the simple theory raises the predicted values for slow burning propellants. This offers a possible explanation for the quantitative discrepancy. It may also be possible that the gas phase chemical reactions may be incomplete under these circumstances, and some energy may be coupled from that source into the acoustic field. However, it must be said that while the simple theory of the response function for a burning propellant gives a generally correct qualitative description of the situation, the question of a complete quantitative description is open. There are also several qualitative phenomena which are not properly explained at this time. Foner, for example, has observed a rise and fall in the amplitude of oscillations in the T-burner, with the periodicity of about one second, for which no satisfactory explanation has been offered.

Before leaving the subject of response function and T-burners, it is important to remark that this technique has given evidence as to the mechanism by which the magic elixir of solid propellants, aluminum, performs its stabilizing role. One of the explanations of the effectiveness of aluminum in preventing acoustic instability was that it produced finely divided aluminum oxide as a smoke in the gas cavity. Very fine smoke particles provide efficient damping of high frequency acoustic waves. In the T-burner it has been observed that the presence of aluminum, at least in some particular propellants, increases the damping in the gas phase while leaving the response function of the burning surface unchanged. This then lends direct support to the particle damping theory.

In discussing the response function, we have been stressing the interaction between the oscillating pressure and the burning rate of the propellant as a source of amplification of the sound wave. The question naturally arises as to whether the acoustic erosion due to the gas velocity associated with the sound wave might not also contribute. Earlier, in discussing a standing tangential wave, we pointed out that the erosive response will be independent of the direction of the gas velocity across the surface. Thus, the erosive response will be positive in both half cycles. The pressure-volume work in one half cycle will be compensated by a negative pressure-volume work in the next half cycle. As a result there will be no contribution from this erosive response to the fundamental frequency of the oscillation. We should observe a change in mean burning rate and the generation of harmonics but no amplification. However, suppose there is mean flow in the direction of the oscillation, as would be true for an axial mode. The superposition of the acoustic velocity upon the mean flow will result in a fluctuation of the velocity across the surface from low to high values, rather than a back and forth flow. In this event it would seem possible that the erosion could contribute a burning response in phase with pressure and thus add to the amplification of the sound wave. However, if one looks at a typical case, for example, the first axial of a cylinder, one finds that the pressure oscillation at the head end is 180° out of phase with the pressure oscillation at the tail end. No corresponding phase shift exists for the velocity component of the standing wave. Thus, if the erosive response in the head end is of an amplifying nature, the erosive response in the tail end is of an equal damping nature. On the grounds of symmetry, therefore, the effect cancels out. Of course, the system is not exactly symmetrical and this cancellation is not exact, but in the main, for low amplitudes, the net result is small.

There are two interesting cases, however, where this symmetry argument does not hold. The first case again has to do with axial modes. The steady state flow velocity in a rocket increases approximately linearly as a function of distance from the head end as more and more gas is added to the stream. Now, if we have an axial mode of high enough amplitude, the velocity associated with the acoustic wave may exceed the flow velocity in magnitude in the front end of the cavity, but not exceed it in the rear. Then flow reversible will occur in the head end but not at the tail end. The symmetry we have discussed will thus be destroyed and an erosive contribution to the amplification to the sound field may be possible. One can work out a simple theory for this phenomenon and show that it can lead to situations where waves below a critical amplitude will be damped, whereas waves above this critical amplitude will grow until they reach another and higher critical amplitude. This represents a rather simple form of nonlinear instability; that is, the system will be stable to small perturbations but if given a high enough triggering impulse, will develop a wave that grows to high amplitude. Such phenomena are indeed observed experimentally, particularly in rockets which are long compared to their diameter and it is highly likely that this feature of nonlinear erosion plays a significant part in such cases.

The second example takes us back to the case of exciting a traveling tangential mode by a peripheral gas jet. Here we are providing a steady state flow around the cylinder so that again we have a mean flow in the direction of the acoustic oscillation, which we saw above was a requirement for coupling by means of acoustic erosivity. In this case the symmetry problem does not occur, for in the traveling wave the velocity is always in phase with the pressure and thus there is no cancellation. A plausible explanation thus is given for the excitation of a traveling tangential by a peripheral gas jet. It should be noted that the traveling wave then induces its own vortex flow, so that the contribution of acoustic erosivity to the instability can be maintained.

THE BALANCE OF GAINS AND LOSSES

The question of acoustic stability in a rocket motor is a question of the balance of acoustic gains and losses. Acoustic losses may occur by transmission of sound through the nozzle or through the wall, or by loss of heat to exposed metal surfaces, or by absorption of sound in the gas phase, or by absorption of sound by the viscoelastic motion of the solid propellant itself. The acoustic gains may arise through the interaction of the pressure or velocity component of the sound field with the burning surface, the extraction of energy from unburned gas in the chamber, or through the transmission of sound from the outside through the case into the motor. The latter appears to explain some instances in which motors stable in ground testing seem to go into unstable burning in certain aerodynamic regimes of flight. It is suggested that the aerodynamic screech of the missile as it flies through the air may, at certain times, coincide in frequency with a fundamental mode of the interior of the motor. While the system would ordinarily be stable, it may have a very high Q, that is, an ability to store a large amount of acoustic energy. In this case the transmission of vibrations through the walls of the motor to the interior at the appropriate frequency would drive the system inside to very high amplitude, and the consequences would be indistinguishable from ordinary instability.

Our ability to predict the various gains and losses with high precision is limited and thus while a qualitative understanding of the phenomenon exists there does not exist quantitative knowledge sufficient to provide the engineer with detailed design criteria. It should also be noted that each of the gains and losses tends to scale with dimensions in its own way. Thus the criterion for stability has no simple scaling and the stability of a scale model in no way guarantees the stability of the full size system. This is the reason why instability in rocket motors has been such an expensive development problem. Since insufficient work has been done to provide the scaling factors for each of the components of the system, instability has had to be faced on full scale and cured by semi-empirical means at that scale. This is true in both solid and liquid systems.

Liquid Fueled Motors

While I have chosen in these lectures to go into considerable detail with respect to acoustic instability in solid rocket motors, for completeness I shall close with a few remarks about the situation in liquid motors. A great deal of work has been done in this area. Among the many working in this field, particular mention should be made of Crocco and his colleagues at Princeton, who have pioneered for many years in this work, and Levine at Rocketdyne who has done much work on practical injection systems.

Much of the general discussion given above on acoustic instability in solid rocket motors is directly applicable to the phenomenon in liquid motors. The same types of acoustic modes occur and with comparable amplitudes. Both systems show excessive vibration when high amplitude waves are present. In the liquid case, however, the excessive operating pressures normally do not occur because the fuel flow is controlled by the injection system, so that a change in a mean fuel rate as observed in the solid case does not occur. For liquid motors, the most disastrous effect is the excessive heat transfer in the presence of the acoustic field and its associated flows. This brings about destruction of the motor by burning through the metal.

Over the years practical experience has led designers to empirical bases for designing motors that are generally stable in the linear domain, that is, small disturbances are damped out. The common instabilities now encountered are nonlinear, that is, sufficiently large perturbations lead to growth of high amplitude waves.

The sensitive region in the liquid fuel motor is the injection zone. Here we have streams of oxidizer and fuel which have not yet been mixed. They thus represent a supply of chemical energy to be tapped by the acoustic field. Motion of the gas across the face of the injector plate, if sufficiently violent, can cause increased atomization of the fuel and oxidizer in this region and thereby promote extra release of energy. At least part of this release of energy may be so phased as to drive the wave. The injector zone region is thus peculiarly sensitive to the velocities associated with transverse waves. Motion pictures taken by Levine at Rocketdyne in transparent walled motors clearly show the dramatic effects of transverse waves on the injection zone. Baffles to protect the injection zone from acoustic fields of this kind are one of the common devices used to correct instability in liquid fuel motors. Changes in the pattern of injection also often relieves the difficulties. The approach is at best semi-empirical and almost always time consuming and expensive.

As with the solid fuel, it might be reasonable to hope that injectors could be described in terms of their response to pressure and velocity oscillations in an analytical way. Research along these lines moves very slowly but provides the only reasonable hope for soundly based design principles.

X. The Stability of Nonlinear Dynamical Systems

JOSEPH P. LA SALLE

HISTORICAL INTRODUCTION

THE FIRST mathematical analysis of the design of feedback control systems is of rather recent origin and dates back to the middle of the nineteenth century. It was Maxwell[1] (for a reprint of this paper see[2]) and independently the Russian engineer, Vishnegradskii[3] who first realized and demonstrated that the design of feedback control mechanisms could be subjected to mathematical analysis. Maxwell entitled his paper "On Governors", whereas the Russian gave his paper the imposing title "On the General Theory of Regulators".

The system to be regulated and the feedback control were both assumed to be linear. Their criterion for satisfactory operation and for selecting the control parameters was to require that the control error approach zero with increasing time (asymptotic stability). This linear analysis for design is then relatively simple. The problem is an algebraic one. The requirement for asymptotic stability is that the roots of a certain polynomial, called the "characteristic polynomial", all have negative real parts. Maxwell was able to give necessary and sufficient conditions that the roots of a polynomial of degree 3 have negative real parts and was also able to give necessary conditions for polynomials of degree 5.

Maxwell then posed in 1868 the problem of finding necessary and sufficient conditions for polynomials of arbitrary degree that their roots have negative real parts. Computable necessary and sufficient

JOSEPH P. LA SALLE is Professor of Applied Mathematics at Brown University, and Director of the Center for Dynamical Systems. Dr. La Salle is an AFOSR grantee and a former president of the Society for Industrial and Applied Mathematics. He was one of the pioneers of the mathematical theory of optimal control. His continuing interests have been on the theory of differential equations and the mathematical theory of control and stability.

conditions were given by Routh in 1877 and by Hurwitz in 1895. In 1911 Bompiani showed the equivalence of the conditions by Routh and by Hurwitz and they are today referred to as the Routh-Hurwitz conditions. Within the last few years it has also been shown that these conditions can be derived using Liapunov's Second Method.

Through World War II the mathematical analysis and the design of feedback control systems was still carried out by an examination of the stability of the linear approximation plus linear feedback. This was, for example, the way in which Minorsky designed an automatic steering device for the battleship *New Mexico* in the early 1920's. More sophisticated analytic, algebraic and geometric tools became available and some consideration was given to performance criteria, but otherwise the analysis was essentially the same as that of Maxwell and Vishnegradskii. This is not to say that successful control devices were not designed by this linear analysis; they certainly were and still are being so designed today. An excellent account of linear stability analysis can be found in Bellman.[4]

Progress in the design of more sophisticated devices depends upon going beyond this linear theory. One method for doing this is to take into account the nonlinearities of the system; that is, to drop the assumption that the control error is small, allow nonlinear feedback and then to carry out a nonlinear analysis of stability. The only general method that we have for doing this was developed by the Russian mathematician Liapunov around 1890.[5] For an elementary account of Liapunov's theory see La Salle and Lefschetz.[6] Starting around 1945 extensive use was made in the Soviet Union of Liapunov's method to investigate the stability of nonlinear systems and for over a decade the Soviet Union enjoyed a virtual monopoly in exploiting and developing Liapunov's theory. In 1944 the Soviet engineers, A. I. Lurie and V. N. Posnokoff, formulated the problem of absolute stability of a certain class of nonlinear control systems and Lurie gave a partial solution to this problem. The nonlinear feedback is not specified but belongs to a wide class of functions. The designer has at his disposal the choice of certain feedback parameters and the problem is to find sufficient conditions on these parameters in order that the error, no matter how large it be, tend to zero with time for any arbitrary nonlinear characteristic in the admissible class. A complete account of this, called absolute stability, can be found in the monograph by Lefschetz.[7] This has been one of the most successful applications of Liapunov's theory.

A letter written by Prof. A. Letov of the Soviet Institute for Automation and Remote Control in Moscow and published in *Regelungstechnik,* 12(1964) had this to say:

> "The year 1945 stands out quite sharply as a turning point in the development of control theory. The control problem suddenly became the object of study by mathematicians. As a basis of their considerations of this problem they selected the concepts of disturbed and undisturbed motions of Liapunov along with the stronger concept of the stability of motion, the quality of the transient behavior, the concept of optimal control, etc. This arose from a need to have an unlimited region of controllability. Liapunov's concept had for more than 50 years found no application in control technology. But now it is characteristic of the present state of control theory that all of its problems—stability, quality of transient behavior, optimization, programmed control—are being considered on the basis of these concepts. These control problems are considered not only for small errors in control but also for finite and often even for arbitrary errors in control. Their solutions draw more and more upon the powerful mathematical methods of linear algebra, the theory of differential equations and topology."

A second and more recent development has been the founding of a mathematical theory of optimal control. There is a system to be controlled and its mathematical model is a system of differential equations. Feedback control introduces into this system of differential equations a function, the control law, which with some limitations, such as limited power, the designer can select. There is also given some criterion of performance. The problem is then to determine which control law gives in terms of the criterion the best performance. The modern development of this theory began with a Princeton Ph.D. dissertation in 1952 by Donald Bushaw.[8] He took a simple problem, solved it, and this began a modern theory of optimal processes. The system to be controlled was linear with one degree of freedom. The control force which could be applied to the system was assumed to operate from a limited source of power, and it was also assumed that the best control would at all times use all the power available ("bang-bang" control) and the criterion for performance was to reduce the control error to zero in the shortest possible time. Bushaw's solution of this restricted problem could not be generalized, but it was his work that brought the problem to the attention of mathematicians, both in the United States and the Soviet Union. For example, in the Soviet Union the work of Pontryagain and his colleagues at the Steklov Mathematics Institute in Moscow won for them in 1962 the Lenin Prize for Science and Technology.

Shortly after the importance of Liapunov's theory of stability and the theory of optimal control were recognized the two began to coalesce. For example, in 1960 Kalman and Bertram[9] pointed out that, for a linear problem of optimal control, if the performance criteria are properly selected, optimal control will imply asymptotic stability, and asymptotic stability is certainly a necessary requirement for the satisfactory performance of a control system. Conversely, it can also be shown that if a feedback control can be designed using Liapunov's method, then, depending upon the Liapunov function used, a certain performance criterion has been optimized. An account of this which contains numerous references can be found in Geiss.[10]

The question is now, where do we stand today? Where do we go from here? It is certainly true that there have been successful applications of the theory and it may perhaps be true that the extent of the applications is much greater than we think. In this country there is security and also the proprietary rights of industry. The situation with regard to open publication is undoubtedly more restricted in the Soviet Union than here and the time delay between the application of theory in the Soviet Union and our awareness of it is anywhere from five to ten years.

But even though there have been some successes we are still highly restricted in applying this theory by our inability to develop computational procedures which enable us to utilize the capabilities of present-day computers in designing control systems. The Liapunov method is the only general method available to us today for analyzing stability and taking into account the nonlinearities of the system, yet the best we have been able to do is to solve a fairly large number of specialized problems. This has been done without the aid of computers. These can be catalogued and they are useful, but it is like having a table of integrals and not being able to compute numerically any given integral. Despite Soviet claims to the contrary, we do not yet know how to use computers to aid us in applying Liapunov's method. There are a number of reasons why it is difficult to do so.

The simplest stability problem is that of determining whether or not a certain equilibrium state is stable or unstable. When everything about the system is known a computer could be used to compute solutions but if the dimension of the system is greater than two or if the system is time-varying, it would be almost impossible to decide stability by computing solutions over a finite interval of time. Another way of saying this is that the significant stability problems require methods that are nonnumerical and the nonnumerical use of computers is not yet highly developed. However, if one thinks about this more realistically, one soon realizes that mathematical asymptotic stability is somewhat different from what the engineer actually wants. Consider for example a control process that acts over only a finite length of time. Mathematical asymptotic stability might suffice to assure satisfactory performance but it is asking far too much. What one needs is not necessarily an infinite time stability but rather stability over a finite interval of time in the presence of perturbations and with a control error that does not become too large. A theory of finite time stability which is quite similar to Liapunov's theory is now in the process of being developed. There are many reasons for believing that the computational difficulties of using computers to carry out this type of stability analysis can be overcome.

Also when we spoke about the relation between Liapunov's method and optimal control we had in mind control processes acting over an infinite interval of time. Of course, all controls act only a finite time, and there are problems in which it is not even useful conceptionally to consider that the system acts over an infinite length of time. One may, for example, wish to move the system from one state to another in a finite length of time and upon reaching the desired state the control process comes to an end. There is in this regard an interesting unsolved theoretical problem which does have practical consequences. Some finite time optimal control problems can be solved or, whether they be optimal or not, one can produce feedback control laws which will move the system from one state to another in finite time. If the control is to be satisfactory it must possess some stability under perturbations and this is what we expect intuitively of feedback control. As yet there are no general results which state when such finite control implies finite time stability, which in turn assures stability under perturbations. Simple examples and experience show that many types of finite time control do possess a very strong stability under perturbations but as yet there is no general theory.

In applying optimal control theory a major problem here is also using computers to determine optimal control laws. There are difficulties, but at the same time it is a numerical problem and a major need is to develop theory to the point at which computation becomes practical. There are a number of types of optimal control problems where theory has provided sufficient structural information about optimal control that it has been possible to devise numerical methods for computing optimal control laws. In some instances this is being done by making the computer an integral part of the control mechanism.

As a mathematician, I am not actually in a position either to judge or predict how successful present theory has been or will be in its application to the design of control systems. There is, however, one thing that is quite evident today. The theory that I have spoken of so far is widely known to engineers throughout the world and if the theory fails in its application, it will not be because it has not been tried. It has had some success. It has certainly stimulated engineers and undoubtedly it will be useful in the future. But its usefulness is limited and let us see now why this is so, and what appear at the moment to be some of the interesting theoretical areas of research where progress will have practical effects.

The major successes of the Liapunov method have been in studying the stability of autonomous systems; that is, systems whose differential equations do not change with time. In many problems in the stability of motion the differential equations are nonautonomous (time-varying). Within the last decade Liapunov's classical theory has been extended for autonomous systems and from this we have new methods which are easier to apply and which give more information than classical methods. This is not true for nonautonomous systems. It is fairly clear intuitively why the study of systems which change with time are more difficult to study. Let me try to explain briefly why this is so mathematically. Bounded solutions of differential equations approach, as time goes to infinity, a set called its "limit" set. It is this limit set that tells how the system behaves ultimately. For autonomous systems this limit set has the important property that it is made up completely of solutions. It is the exploitation of this fact that has made is possible to unify and extend Liapunov's theory. For nonautonomous systems the limit set does not, in general, have this property and for systems which are time-varying this same extension of Liapunov's theory is not possible. This is an important area for further research and some recent developments in the solution of some particular problems indicate that some progress is certainly possible in the direction of developing both new theory and new methods.

The discussion so far has been limited to systems whose mathematical model is a system of ordinary differential equations. This means that the state (or phase) space is a finite dimensional Euclidean space. If one knows at a given time the values of the state variables, which are finite in number, then the future behavior of the system is completely determined. This is as in classical mechanics. If all the forces acting are known, the motion of a body is completely determined by its initial position and initial velocity. It has also been assumed so far in speaking of controlling or stabilizing a system, that is it possible at each instant of time to measure precisely all of the state variables. This is not always possible. In some cases it may be possible to measure only some function of the state variables and an important class of problems are those which take this fact into account. One may wish, for example, to generate a control law to stabilize a system which is originally unstable, where the control law will depend upon the information available at each time concerning the state of the system and this information may not be complete. This is a general area about which there is not too much theory. It can, however, be shown by simple examples that there are cases where it is not possible to stabilize the system by a control law which, at each instant, depends upon the available measurements of the state variables made at that instant and in order to stabilize the system one must make use of a portion of the past history of these measurements over some interval of time. Now the mathematical model is not longer a system of ordinary differential equations but is a system of what is called "functional differential equations". This is an extension of and includes the classical difference-differential equations (differential equations with delayed arguments). The importance of the effects of delays in analyzing dynamical systems was pointed out quite clearly by Minorsky.[11] These equations have also been called "hereditary" differential equations. The state of such systems is now no longer a point in a finite dimensional

Euclidean space (that is, a finite set of numbers) but is a function and the state space is now a function space (an infinite dimensional space). This point of view seems to have been introduced by Krasovskii and using this point of view he extended to functional differential equations almost all of the classical Liapunov theory.[12] However, from the point of view of applications, Krasovskii's results are not very useful. Now, more recently, Hale has obtained results which give methods that can be applied and he has demonstrated this by numerous examples.[13] This is a very challenging field for research and a number of mathematicians throughout the world are working on developing the theory of functional differential equations. At the moment the general aim of the research is to see how much of our knowledge of ordinary differential equations can be extended. This has already been done, as I have indicated, for stability theory, and also for certain problems in nonlinear oscillations. Because the state space is now an infinite dimensional space, the mathematics is much more sophisticated, but properly viewed it looks as if a great deal of the theory of ordinary differential equations does carry over. As is to be expected, new phenomena do appear and this is one of the most interesting aspects of the theory. There are already interesting applications to biology, economics, visco-elasticity, nuclear reactors, etc. It would appear that the theory of such equations will play an important role in the future in the study of control and stability. It is hard to imagine a system which will be adaptive in some meaningful sense unless it makes use at all times of all the past information that is available.

This is still a deterministic theory and as such is not entirely realistic. A system is never known perfectly. There are always errors in the measurement of state variables and there are always perturbations (noise) that cannot be perfectly predicted. This does not mean that systems designed on the basis of a deterministic theory will not work properly. The question is, and this is the fundamental problem of stochastic control, can we, if statistical information is available concerning the perturbations, make use of this to improve control. The study of stochastic processes (stochastic differential equations) is relatively new and is primitive compared with our knowledge of ordinary differential equations. Stochastic control theory is still in its infancy. A survey of some recent developments was given by Kushner.[14] With regard to what has been said here today it now appears to be true that there are stochastic analogs to almost all of the deterministic applications of Liapunov theory to the design of control systems. Independently, this has also been discovered in the Soviet Union. The whole area of stochastic control is one which until quite recently has been neglected in this country. Future progress here will depend not only upon attempts to apply what is already known but, more importantly for the moment, upon the development of a more complete mathematical theory of stochastic processes.

With regard to the theory of stability and optimal control its status appears in summary to be this. During the 1950's there was a rapid development of a theory of optimal control, Liapunov's theory was rediscovered and extended and the importance of carrying out nonlinear analyses of stability was widely recognized. During the last 5-8 years there have been few, if any, startling new ideas. Engineers today (and this was not true 10 years ago) have a general awareness of the theory that exists and its possible applications, and from the point of view of applications the biggest hurdle here is learning how to use computers to apply the theory. The Liapunov theory of stability for autonomous systems has been unified and extended and would appear to be fairly complete. Further developments of theory for nonautonomous systems seem possible. For the study of the stability of nonautonomous linear systems new methods have been found but there are no new ideas in sight other than those generated by Liapunov's method for carrying out nonlinear stability analyses. Of much greater promise is the study of more "practical" types of stability and here the use of computers should be much less difficult. Two relatively new and promising areas of mathematical research in which some progress has already been made are the theory of functional differential equations and the theory of stochastic differential equations. Developments here could have a profound effect on the theory of control systems and the theory of systems in general. From the point of view of the mathematician, the problem of adaptation and learning has not yet been satisfactorily formulated and what one should do here is, like Bushaw, to state the simplest problem precisely and attempt to solve it.

This is not and was not intended to be an all-inclusive list of areas of research which may prove to be important in the design of control systems and is primarily restricted to the role of stability theory in the theory of control. Important areas about which I have said nothing are system identification, dynamic programming, theory of information, nonlinear filtering, statistical decision theory, etc., all of which are areas which have, and probably will continue to have, an important role in the theory of control. No one can predict with any accuracy where the next breakthrough will come.

REFERENCES

[1] Maxwell, J. C., *On governors*, Proc. of the Royal Society of London, 16 (1868), 270-283.

[2] Bellman, R. and Kalaba, R. *Selected Papers on Mathematical Trends in Control Theory*, Dover Publications, Inc., New York, 1964.

[3] Vishnegradskii, J., *Sur la Theorie Generale des Regulateurs*, Compt. Rend. Acad. Sci., Paris, 83 (1876), 318-321.

[4] Bellman, R., *Stability Theory of Differential Equations*, McGraw-Hill Book Co., New York, 1953.

[5] Liapunov, A., *Problème Général de la Stabilité du Mouvement*, (French translation, 1907) photoreproduced, Annals of Mathematics Study No. 17, Princeton University Press, Princeton, New Jersey, 1949.

[6] LaSalle, J. and Lefschetz, S., *Stability by Liapunov's Direct Method with Applications*, Academic Press, New York, 1961.

[7] Lefschetz, S., *Stability of Nonlinear Control Systems*, Academic Press, New York, 1965.

[8] Bushaw, D. W., *Differential equations with a discontinuous forcing term*, Ph.D. Thesis, Dept. of Math., Princeton Univ., 1952; *Optimal discontinuous forcing terms*, Contributions to the Theory of Nonlinear Oscillations, IV, Princeton University Press, 1958.

[9] Kalman, R. and Bertram, J., *Control system analyses and design via the second method of Liapunov*, ASME J. of Basic Eng., June, 1960, 371-393 and 394-422.

[10] Geiss, G. R., *The analysis and design of nonlinear control systems via Liapunov's direct method*, Technical Documentary Report No. RTD-TDR-63-4076, Air Force Flight Dynamics Laboratory, Research and Technology Division, USAF, Wright-Patterson Air Force Base, Ohio, August, 1964.

[11] Minorsky, N., *Self-excited oscillations in dynamical systems possessing retarded actions*, J. of Appl. Mech., 9 (1942), 65-71. A reprint can be found in [2].

[12] Krasovskii, N. N., *Stability of Motion*, Moscow, 1959. English translation, Stanford Univ. Press, 1963.

[13] Hale, J., *Sufficient conditions for stability and instability of autonomous functional differential equations*, to appear in Journal of Differential Equations.

[14] Kushner, H. J., *Some Problems and Some Recent Results in Stochastic Control*, 1965 IEEE Int'l Convention Record, Part VI, 108-116.

XI. Tides of The Planet Earth

WALTER H. MUNK

HISTORICAL INTRODUCTION

QUITE GOOD predictions of ocean tides were made a century ago by the nonharmonic method initiated by Lubbock. This uses multiple regressions, such as

height of high water = mean height above datum
+ correction for age of Moon + correction for declination (1)
+ correction for parallax + diurnal inequality + . . .

The method is based on the high correlation between pertinent tidal and lunar parameters, a correlation that was known and used long before the time of Newton.

The next development was the harmonic method by Kelvin and George Darwin. Tides are predicted for any given port as a sum of sinusoids:

$$\zeta(t) = \sum_k C_k \cos(2\pi f_k t + \theta_k). \qquad (2)$$

The frequencies f_k are derived from astronomic observations and are essentially sums and differences of the six basic frequencies in the motions of Earth, Moon, and Sun: the day, month, year, 8.9 years (lunar perigee), 18.6 years (lunar nodes), and 21,000 years (solar perigee). The harmonic method has two shortcomings: it does not allow for the "noisy" variations in sea level associated with atmospheric pressure and winds, and it does not allow for the distortion of the tides as they move into shallow water. The latter feature can, to some extent, be taken into account by introducing additional sums and differences of the six basic frequencies, but there was a practical limit to the number of terms in Eq. (2), usually between 30 and 60.

WALTER H. MUNK, Professor of Geophysics at the University of California, San Diego, and director of the La Jolla Laboratories of the Institute of Geophysics and Planetary Physics; serving on a President's Science Advisory Committee panel on earthquake prediction; AFOSR grantee, originator of the Mohole Project.

SPECTROSCOPY OF TIDES

The complexity of the harmonic method is in a sense an artifice arising from our insistence to expand the tide-producing potential as a strictly harmonic series. With modern computing machines it is much easier to generate the tide-producing potential hour-by-hour directly from the known positions of Earth, Moon, and Sun, and pay no attention to the fact that the resulting time series appears to have a complicated spectral structure. Call this artificial times series $x(t)$, and the observed series $y(t)$. The spectra of $x(t)$ shows a cluster of spectral lines centered at 0, 1, 2 cycles per day; within each cluster there is first-order splitting by 1 cycle per month, and each of these lines is further split by 1 cycle per year, etc. For the moment, the interesting thing is that between these measured clusters the energy density is very low, down by a million or more from the peak of the cluster. The spectrum of the observed series $y(t)$ looks very similar except that now the region between clusters is filed by a fairly uniform continuum. This continuum represents the irregular oscillation in sea level arising from non-astromocic sources.

PREDICTION BY THE RESPONSE METHOD

The most elementary way in describing the response of a physical system is to plot output energy divided by input energy as a function of frequency. We do this by substracting the noise contribution from the observed spectral lines (thus being left with "coherent" energy), comparing this to the appropriate input energy. The response functions $w^2(f)$ we obtain in this manner are reasonably smooth functions of frequency, with no sharp resonances apparent.

This suggests a different method of prediction than the classical harmonic method. We use past port observations to obtain the response curves $w(f)$ of a port, and then obtain future predictions by playing the theoretical tide input $x(t)$ through the appropriate response filter (this is done numerically, using computers):

$$y(t) = \sum_k x(t - \tau_k) g(\tau_k) \tag{3}$$

with $g(\tau)$ the Fourier transform of $w(f)$.

There is some additional complication arising from the fact that there is a multiplicity of input functions $x_i(t)$, each corresponding to a spherical-harmonic of the tide potential, and we require separate response filters $w_i(f)$ for each of these time-dependent harmonics; but this does not cause any real difficulty. The spherical-harmonic expansion converges rapidly, and just a few terms will do. The important thing is that there is no time-harmonic expansion, as the complexity of the tide-potential is already built into the input functions $x_i(t)$. The advantage of the response method over the harmonic method is that it takes full account of Newton-Kepler mechanics, while the harmonic method uses astronomy only to identify the frequencies f_k. There are additional advantages insofar as the response method can be systematically generalized to include the non-linear shallow water effects. It may even be possible to include the response to storms.

New Developments

The spectroscopy and prediction just described has been made possible by the development of modern computers. In this way hourly times series extending over 50 years and comprising some 500,000 observations can be readily and adequately analyzed. Computers have also opened the possibility for solving the "theoretical tide problem": to compute the deep sea tides, given the configuration of the ocean basins and the positions of Moon and Sun. This is obviously a very cumbersome boundary value problem. The first attempt was made by Pekeris a few years ago. Definitive results are not yet available but will be before the decade is up.

Another new development is the instrumentation for measuring tides in the deep sea, now being carried out in France and at La Jolla. All we do now is to measure tides at given ports. This is where one needs the observation for predictions at this port, but it is the worst place for the theoretical tide problem. Here one would like to cover the oceans with some observational grid, 1,000 km $\times$ 1,000 km $\times$ one month, say, and thus determine the "cotidal" lines. A comparsion with the theoretical deep sea tides will be most illuminating.

The average tidal bulge must lag somewhat behind the theoretical bulge as the result of dissipative processes, mostly in marginal seas. One can then compute the decelerating torque affecting the spin of the Earth, and the accelerating torque on the Moon's orbital motion. Comparison with astronomic observations will show whether the ocean tides are responsible for the measured changes in the Moon's angular velocity, or whether the bodily tides of the Earth play an important additional role. In the former case one cannot extrapolate the present rate over more than a million years because of the effect of changing sea level. In the latter case one can extrapolate much further. Studies by Wells of Devonian coral indicate that the present rate can be extrapolated 400 million years, and this is surprising in view of the fact that we believe most of the tidal dissipation takes place in the shallow oceans.

The Changing Face of the Earth's Surface

If we could view the surface of the Earth through time-lapsed photographs at intervals of one century, we would be impressed with the variability of surface features. Mountains rise, valleys broaden, and perhaps continents shift apart, with typical velocities of 1 cm/year. Modern gravimeters and associated instrumentation which were developed to measure the tides of the solid Earth will soon be good enough to record changes even slower than those of the tides. It is here where ultra-low-frequency seismology turns into ultra-high-frequency geology. This fascinating subject is just now being made accessible. Studying dynamic geology by the present indirect methods is like studying ocean currents without current meters and the atmosphere without anemometers. Even with current meters and anemometers available, we haven't done too well in describing and understanding the moving oceans and atmosphere; without such instrumentation we would have done very poorly indeed, and this is precisely where geology now finds itself in its attempt to describe and explain the changing Earth from indirect evidence only.

Conclusions and Summary

The developments of new technologies and instrumentations have given us new opportunities to study the tidal distortion of the planet Earth, and this promises to bring back to life a subject which has been dormant for half a century. It appears as if the instrumentation developed for this purpose will be able to cope also with the distortions of the Earth on a geological time scale.

XII. High Field Magnets and Magnetospectroscopy

BENJAMIN LAX

I HIGH FIELD MAGNETS

SCIENTIFIC investigation with magnetic fields on a quantitative basis had its origin during the nineteenth century. Among the outstanding pioneers, the contributions of Faraday, Zeeman and Weiss are particularly pertinent to the subject matter of this discourse. The discoveries of these physicists gave an impetus to the early development of electromagnets of increasing intensity which at that time represented a milestone in the history of high field magnets. The famous Weiss electromagnet with its iron yoke and pole pieces energized by twin coils still remains the basic design for the modern commercial electromagnets available today. The highest fields achieved by such a design is that of the large Cotton magnet at Bellevue, France, built in 1912, capable of producing a field of the order of 60 kilogauss between pole faces approximately 5 millimeters apart when energized by coils at 100 kilowatts. This magnet is matched only by a similar one at Uppsala, Sweden.

The next advance in high field development also took place in France in 1914 when Delandres and Perot[1] constructed a large water-cooled "jelly roll" solenoid able to produce 70 kilogauss for a short period when energized from a 500 kilowatt generator. The outbreak of World War II prevented the continuation of this effort beyond its initial phase. Nevertheless, it laid the foundation for subsequent developments of water-cooled coils.

BENJAMIN LAX, Director, National Magnet Laboratory, operated for AFOSR by the Massachusetts Institute of Technology. This laboratory is the world's foremost facility for the study of matter under the influence of intense magnetic fields. Its 250,000 gauss device produces the most intense continuous magnet fields attainable. Dr. Lax is a prolific researcher in solid state physics and a former associate director of the Lincoln Laboratory.

The advent of high field magnets as we know them today took place in Cambridge, England, in the 1920's when the famous Russian physicist Peter Kapitza devised two ingenious schemes for generating pulsed fields.[2] The first technique involved the discharge of batteries by a mechanical switch through a wire-wound solenoid to produce 500 kilogauss for a few milliseconds in a very small volume, and the second by shorting a large generator into a somewhat larger coil to produce over 300 kilogauss. He used these magnets for low temperature magnetoresistance measurements and for Faraday rotation observations.

The next important development was due to Francis Bitter[3] at the Massachusetts Institute of Technology. He designed and built a water-cooled magnet capable of producing 100 kilogauss continuously in an internal diameter of one inch using a generator which delivered 1.7 megawatts. The magnet was intended primarily for the study of atomic Zeeman spectroscopy. The basic design consists of radially cut copper plates interspersed with insulating discs, both of which are assembled to generate an intertwined double helix of overlapping plates, as shown in Fig. 1. These are housed under compression in a metal jacket so that the water flows axially through

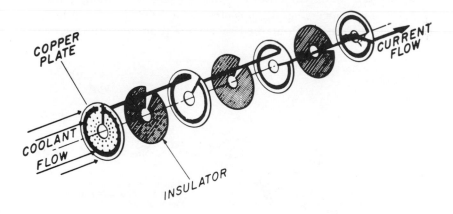

PRINCIPLE OF THE BITTER SOLENOID

FIGURE 1. Configuration of the conducting and insulating discs of the Bitter coil arranged in an intertwined helical pattern.

perforations in the disc. This basic design was duplicated at the Naval Research Laboratory in 1947, and elsewhere throughout the world since.

The post-World War II period, beginning in the 1950's, witnessed a renaissance in the development of high field magnets and their application to scientific research. Six different techniques have been explored, namely, iron core magnets, pulse systems, cryogenic magnets, water-cooled coils, superconducting magnets, and implosion systems. The iron core magnets have become a commercial item for a large variety of resonance experiments with maximum fields of the order of 50 kilogauss between tapered pole pieces with about one-quarter inch spacing. However, for larger useful volumes and uniform fields, the intensity is limited to about 20 kilogauss.

A.   PULSED MAGNETS

One of the most important steps taken to advance high field magnet technology occurred in 1956 in the area of pulse magnets. Furth and Waniek[4] at Harvard constructed a nitrogen cooled pulsed magnet using a Bitter disc arrangement which ultimately reached 600 kilogauss. This was exceeded by Foner and Kolm[5] who achieved 750 kilogauss in a room temperature helical coil made of a single piece of beryllium-copper (Fig. 2), powered by a 9,000 joule condenser bank. The highest field obtained by a large condenser pulse system

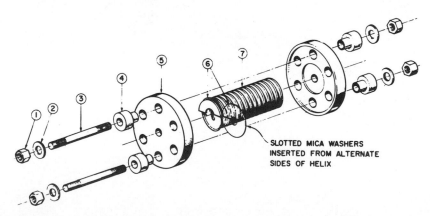

FIGURE 2. A sketch of the component parts of the copper berrylium pulse magnet designed by Foner and Kolm for producing fields between 300 and 750,000 gauss. (After Foner and Kolm, ref. 5).

was that by Furth, Waniek, and Levine,[6] who generated about 1.5 megagauss in a single turn coil. Today there are many pulse coils of different dimensions and designs which produce fields of the order of 100 to 500 kilogauss for experimental use in working volumes up to one-inch diameter and time duration of microseconds to several milliseconds. However, the largest fields available today are those generated by implosion techniques.[7] This involves the concept of flux compression through a physical magnetohydrodynamic phenomenon in which the magnetic field is first generated by a pulsed solenoid in a metallic cylindrical liner. This is then collapsed by a chemical explosive which implodes the cylinder and compresses the magnetic flux from about 200 kilogauss to approximately ten to fifteen million gauss. The pressure necessary to contain this field is about 10^7 atmospheres. The field is measured during a ten microsecond interval by a magnetic pickup coil or by Faraday rotation in a quartz rod before they are destroyed by the implosion. It is estimated that approximately 100 megagauss should be possible by this method of generating high fields.

B. Water-cooled Magnets

For about twenty-five years no significant advancement was made in the generation of high fields by water-cooled magnets beyond that attained by Bitter in 1936. A group of solid state physicists from the MIT Lincoln Laboratory joined forces with Bitter in 1958 and proposed the creation of a quarter million gauss facility. This was soon championed by a far-sighted group in the Air Force who, with an assist from the Department of Defense, agreed to sponsor the design and construction of such a laboratory. In 1960 a contract was drawn up with the Air Force to begin this project for a high field facility. Soon afterwards, under the sponsorship of the Air Force Office of Scientific Research, simultaneously with the design of a new laboratory, a program of research and development began at the old MIT laboratory. Improved Bitter magnets were developed and innovations in the control system and cooling were incorporated. This laboratory became a test bed for many new developments which have been incorporated into the new laboratory. One of the highlights was the development of a 126 kilogauss tape-wound magnet by Kolm in 1961 with only 1.9 megawatts. This was exceeded in 1962 by the Naval Research Laboratory in a Bitter magnet at a 3 megawatt power level which yielded 150 kilogauss in a one-inch bore.[8] Construction of the new National Magnet Laboratory, begun in 1961, was completed in the spring of 1963. After a shakedown test period and subsequent improvements, the laboratory began as an operating facility in the fall of that year.

The National Magnet Laboratory,[9] which is located within the MIT campus complex in Cambridge, is linked to the Charles River basin by two 48-inch concrete pipe lines for providing primary cooling water for the magnets. The secondary system contains deionized, distilled water which is pumped through copper pipes and a large heat exchanger. The power for the magnets is provided by two sets of motor generators which are capable of delivering ten million watts of 250 volt power continuously to the magnets. In addition, the system has a pulse capability of 32 megawatts for a few seconds by using energy stored in two ninety-ton flywheels. The four generators can be connected from the control room in series-parallel combinations to any of ten magnet stations. Four independent experiments at one-quarter power, or two at one-half power and one at full power can be operated at any given time. There are some twenty magnets ranging from 70 to 200 kilogauss which can accommodate about two dozen experiments per week.

Two basic designs of water-cooled magnets are employed at the laboratory.[10] The first of these is the modified Bitter axially cooled magnet shown in Fig. 3. One such magnet, consisting of two nested sets of plates, one with a four-inch internal diameter, the other with a one-inch internal diameter, is capable of producing 180 kilogauss with two generators at a power level of five megawatts. The other design is an innovation in which the copper discs have radial cooling slots and, again, are wound in helices similar to the Bitter solenoids. The insulating helix is made of stainless steel discs (coated with insulation) for greater strength, as shown in Fig. 4. One version of this type of magnet composed of three nested coils with an overall dimension of about three feet and the internal diameter of two inches, has provided 205 kilogauss at full power of 10 megawatts. With iron pole pieces inserted, it has achieved the record continuous field of 255 kilogauss. Another important feature of this basic design is that it has allowed for a flexible configuration of a split pair of coils whose spacing is variable. These magnets are exceedingly useful for optical experiments in which longitudinal and transverse access to the field is required.

C. Low Temperature Magnets

There are two types of low temperature magnets that have been under development during the last decade. The first of these is the cryogenic magnet in which a low temperature cooling liquid, such as hydrogen or neon, is used to lower the resistivity of such materials as copper and aluminum. Such cooling was first used with pulse systems[11] to produce fields as high as 100 kilogauss. The hydrogen system has been used at Los Alamos[12] and by the National Bureau of Standards at Boulder.[13] The resistivity of copper is lowered by a factor of 100 at 20°K. The system requires a large liquid hydrogen

FIGURE 3. Sketch of a magnet station in the new National Magnet Laboratory, showing water connections from a hydrant and electrical terminals. The inset shows the type of Bitter plates used in modern magnets to produce fields of 100 to 180,000 gauss.

storage tank and a low voltage high current source of power of the order of 5 to 10 volts. Homopolar generators have provided power for the magnets. At Los Alamos a maximum field of about 80 kilogauss at 12,000 amperes and 25 kilowatts has been achieved with a "jelly roll" copper coil. Each run requires about 3,000 to 5,000 liters of liquid hydrogen and allows for twenty minute operation per run. Aluminum has also been used by the group at the Bureau of Standards since its magnetoresistance at high fields is less than that of copper. However, the magnet is comparable in performance to the copper system. The most elaborate scheme for a cryogenic magnet is that at the NASA Lewis Research Center[14] which also employs aluminum, but at liquid neon temperatures of about 27°K. Al-

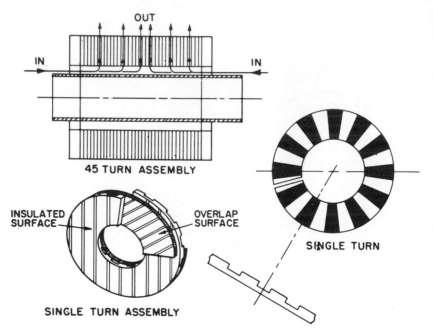

RADIALLY COOLED SOLENOID (INNER
COIL SECTION OF 250 KG MAGNET)

FIGURE 4. Basic design and concept of the radial cooled magnets. These are employed in a concentrically nested arrangement in the 250,000 gauss magnet and pairs for transverse access optical magnets. (After Montgomery, ref. 21).

though this has some thermodynamic advantages over hydrogen, it is very expensive. Nevertheless, a large volume coil of approximately 4½ inch internal diameter was operated at a 200 kilogauss level for one minute. The re-liquifaction time of the neon system limits the duty cycle to about one minute in every twenty-four hours. The power supply is a one megawatt homopolar generator.

In the low temperature field perhaps the most important development has been that of the superconducting magnets. The possibility of such a device was conceived in 1913 by Kamerlingh Onnes, the discoverer of superconductivity.[15] However, although a few isolated attempts were made in the interim, very little was done until 1960 when serious work at Lincoln Laboratory was carried out to provide niobium coils of 10 kilogauss and small iron core magnets with niobium windings giving up to 25 kilogauss for maser applications.[16] In 1961 at the Bell Telephone Laboratories, Kunsler and co-workers[17] demonstrated that niobium tin was superconducting at about 90 kilogauss. Subsequent pulse measurements indicated an upper limit near 200 kilogauss. This material was soon followed by niobium zirconium and more recently by niobium titanium. The latter two have been commercially used to develop magnets of the order of about 60 kilogauss in niobium zirconium for operation in a one-inch diameter and 80 kilogauss in niobium titanium in a comparable volume. These coils are built in nested concentric sections. Perhaps the most significant achievement in terms of high fields with superconducting magnets has been that with niobium tin in which fields of the order of 130 kilogauss in a one-inch diameter have been achieved by General Electric.[18] In larger volumes of the order of about six inches diameter, fields of the order of 60 kilogauss have been attained at Argonne[19] with the use of copper inserts to overcome flux trappings and heating effects which ordinarily limit the use of superconducting magnets.

D. Present Status and Future Possibilities

At the present time the status of magnets may be summarized by the two charts shown in Figs. 5 and 6. The first of these[20] indicates that for water-cooled magnets in a working volume of about two inches, which appears to be the standard today, the water-cooled magnets provide fields of 200 kilogauss, the cryogenic magnets half that field, and the superconducting magnets somewhat less. If we take into account both the size of the field and the intensity, the second chart of Fig. 6[21] shows that iron core magnets are useful up to about 20 kilogauss at these and larger volumes, that superconducting magnets should ultimately be capable of providing fields at these and larger volumes in the future, up to perhaps 100 kilogauss. For very high fields only the pulse systems are possible and these will ultimately provide fields of the order of 1 million gauss in small volumes. As far as the future goes, it appears that for practical experimental purposes in terms of effectiveness, the water-cooled magnets, the superconducting magnets, and the pulse magnets will play important roles in the order mentioned. With our present knowledge of materials and engineering know-how, the water-cooled magnets appear most promising for high continuous fields and also for intermittent repetitive pulse operation. For the former it is estimated that fields of the order of 500 kilogauss are conceivable in comfortable working volumes at a power level somwhere between 100 and 200 megawatts. Intermittent repetitive pulse fields of this order are also possible at existing power levels, and it is expected that such magnets capable of achieving 300 kilogauss or more will be developed at NML in the near future.

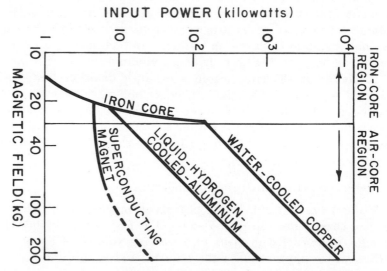

FIGURE 5. Present capabilities of different magnets in a two-inch working volume. (After Hulm, ref. 20).

Insofar as superconducting magnets are concerned, present limitations indicate about 170 kilogauss with niobium tin. It is expected that these will be used as inserts in water-cooled magnets for certain experimental arrangements which will enable a greater efficiency of the power plant at NML, thus providing magnets of this field level on a single 2.5 megawatt generator. Ultimately, it is hoped that large volume superconducting magnets providing 50 to 100 kilogauss will be engineered to enclose water-cooled magnets and thereby boost the maximum field by this magnitude. This combination is optimum since it appears that only water-cooled magnets using beryllium-copper or chromium copper will stand up at fields in excess of one-quarter million gauss. Superconducting magnets in large volumes, of course, will ultimately be constructed and will play an increasingly important role in the operation of cloud chambers and magnetohydrodynamic generators. New configurations, including Helm-

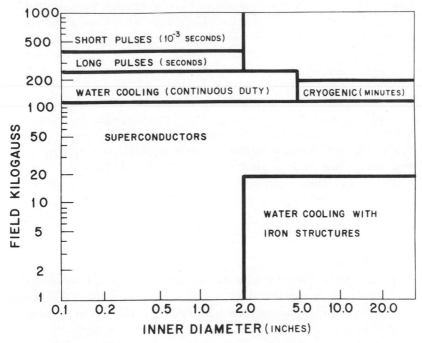

FIGURE 6. Chart of field intensities versus size for different magnet systems. (After Montgomery, ref. 21).

holtz pairs, radial access magnets, and air core solenoids, using superconducting coils, will become available. With the appropriate refrigerating systems, undoubtedly these will be somewhat expensive.

II MAGNETOSPECTROSCOPY

Research with high magnetic fields at the National Magnet Laboratory is expected over the next decade to cover a broad area of science, not only by the scientists in residence, but also by a large group of visitors. These areas naturally include the magnet research and development which was discussed in Section I; solid state physics, which will be treated in detail; and related low temperature physics, which is just beginning. Atomic and molecular spectroscopy, although one of the oldest areas to utilize high magnetic fields, will undoubtedly be revived, particularly in connection with laser research in gases. Plasma physics, both in solid state and gaseous plasmas, has traditionally been closely associated with magnetic fields. However, as yet only modest efforts with high intensity fields have been attempted. Resonance phenomena of electrons and ions, plasma waves, diffusion effects, etc., will be investigated above 100 kilogauss in the future with greater precision and resolution. High magnetic fields can be used very advantageously in nuclear physics for nuclear resonance, the Mössbauer effect, and gamma ray correlation experiments to study nuclear levels and spin values in the ground and excited states with greater sensitivity and precision. In addition, cloud chambers and bubble chambers will require these fields in large volumes for more effective exploration of nuclear and high energy phenomena. Finally, in such fields as biomagnetics, magnetochemistry and metallurgy, it is expected that visitors will continue to use the facilities of NML with increasing frequency to investigate and explore as yet unknown phenomena with the hope of making new and startling discoveries.

A. Solid State Physics

In solid state physics a wide variety of phenomena have already been explored in the broad field which we have named magnetospectroscopy. Among these, such resonance experiments as cyclotron, antiferromagnetic, nuclear, and paramagnetic resonance, etc., will continue to be fruitful research areas for some time. Plasma phenomena in solids involving the interaction of electromagnetic radiation with multicomponent carriers is now of great interest to physicists. Magnetic fields have long been used for the study of steady transport properties such as the Hall effect, magnetoresistance, susceptibility, and thermomagnetic effects. However, recently the study of oscillatory phenomena associated with the quantum nature of electrons in a magnetic field have made these older experimental techniques of great significance in exploring the fundamental nature and properties of electrons in semiconductors and metals. Even more recently acoustical techniques, which will be discussed, have added a new dimension to this important approach to transport studies of these materials. The field of magneto-optical investigations of solids is perhaps the oldest and most celebrated one since it was discovered by Faraday in 1845 and was a keystone in atomic spectroscopy after the discovery of the Zeeman effect at the turn of the century. Nevertheless, an entirely new field of modern magneto-optics has grown up in the last decade, mainly due to the advent of intense magnetic fields, low temperatures, and high purity single crystals. More recently, spectroscopic studies of lasers and the operation of lasers themselves in magnetic fields have further revolutionized this exciting area of physics. Superconductivity at high magnetic fields is not only of practical importance today, but the physics of high field materials is one of the challenging problems and continues to be explored. A wide variety of new materials is constantly being developed and measured at the highest fields available at NML. Magnetism and magnetic properties of materials such as the transition metals, ferrites, antiferromagnets and ferrimagnetics constitute in themselves a major field of science and of course exhibit properties which lend themselves very naturally to exploration at fields of 100 kilogauss or more. The internal fields in these materials are often of this magnitude and, when subjected to external fields comparable or larger, the materials exhibit interesting and anomalous behavior which as yet is not fully understood. One of the tools which serves as an extremely versatile and sensitive probe in this context is the Mössbauer effect in which an ultra-narrow line or band of frequencies in the gamma ray region is emitted. The magnetic environment is reflected in the Zeeman spectrum of these lines and serves as a means for studying the microscopic properties of electrons and nuclei in magnetic materials of all sorts.

B.   Intraband Effects

Physicists began studying the interaction of electromagnetic radiation with electrons in the ionosphere in the presence of the earth's magnetic field about forty years ago. They were among the first to recognize the phenomena of cyclotron resonance, magnetoplasma reflection, and plasma waves. The interesting situation that has developed is that these same phenomena in solids have evolved into a rich and fruitful field of investigation which has been extended into the realm of quantized phenomena. Cyclotron resonance in germanium and silicon at microwave frequencies at low temperatures has triggered a series of theoretical and experimental investigations that have elucidated the band properties of semiconductors and metals and the topology of Fermi surfaces in a most remarkable way.[22] However, in order to extend these measurements to other semiconductors it was necessary to do this at higher frequencies in the infrared and millimeter regions. This was accomplished by developing pulse fields of the order of several hundred thousand gauss. It was soon recognized that steady fields of this order or somewhat smaller and far infrared techniques would be the ideal combination. The partial, but significant, success with the III-V compound semiconductors should be soon augmented when present high fields are combined with lasers in the submillimeter region at 100 to 300 microns. A whole new era for the study of cyclotron resonance in solids will begin.

A phenomenon closely related to cyclotron resonance is that of reflecting electromagnetic waves from an electron plasma in a magnetic field. As the frequency is varied from a low value, the medium is highly reflecting until a critical plasma frequency is reached. Then the medium becomes transparent and at higher frequencies behaves as a dielectric. In a magnetic field this plasma edge on reflection is split into two edges, which are separated from each other by the cyclotron frequency. By carrying out such experiments at infrared wavelengths on a quantitative basis, it is possible to measure the electron density, the electron effective mass, the dielectric constant, and the relaxation time in a semiconductor or semimetal.[23] Plasma phenomena in such materials can also be investigated at high magnetic fields by transmission of helicon waves,[24] which are circularly polarized waves rotating in the same sense as the electron in the magnetic field. The velocity of this wave is proportional to the square root of the magnetic field. Thus by varying the magnetic field, the index of refraction of a slab is altered so that it provides interference at multiples of half wavelengths. By investigating these in a microwave bridge, a very interesting interference pattern is observed from which a highly accurate measurement of the electron density can be obtained[25] as shown in Fig. 7. In semimetals where the electron and hole concentrations are equal, no helicon wave exists, but instead the wave has a velocity which is proportional to the magnetic field.[26] This is known as the Alfvén wave which is found in the ionosphere. Such waves have become very interesting recently in materials such as bismuth, graphite, and other semimetals in high fields.

Other effects such as Faraday rotation and the closely related Kerr magneto-optic effect, in which linearly polarized waves are rotated by electrons in semiconductors, metals and magnetic materials are also of great value to fundamental studies of these materials. Intense magnetic fields will play an ever increasing role in exploring the properties of quasi-free electrons in such solids. Not only will effective masses be measured, but magnetic interaction within the solids will be uncovered.

C. Interband Effects

By interband effects we mean electron transitions induced in crystals between the atomic levels which have been spread into bands and which are separated by regions of forbidden energies. Due to the existence of these quasi-continuous bands or levels, it is difficult to determine the quantitative nature of the energy structure of the crystal. However, with the introduction of a magnetic field, the levels or bands become requantized; furthermore, this is directionally dependent, making such a study a very intriguing and a challenging prospect. Indeed, both absorption and dispersive phenomena at optical and infrared frequencies in solids have opened a new era of magneto-optical investigations unheard of until this decade. A variety of magneto-absorption, Faraday rotation, cross-field magneto-absorption, magneto-reflection, and other related effects have been investigated.[27] In a semiconductor in the presence of an oscillating electric field transverse to the magnetic field, the intrared absorption is very sensitively observed. For the first time the oscillatory effect in

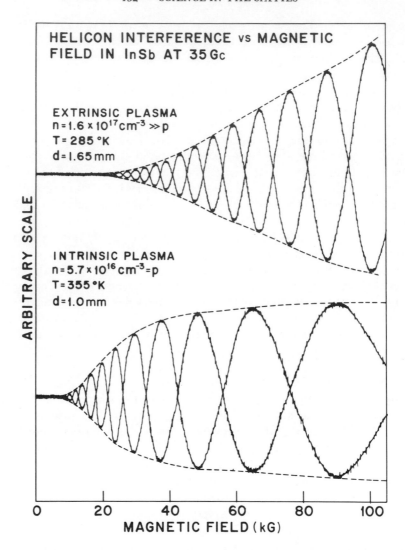

FIGURE 7. Helicon waves in a solid state plasma at microwave frequencies. (After Furdyna, ref. 25).

GaAs has been observed by this new cross-field magneto-absorption[28] as shown in Fig. 8. The oscillations are evidence of the quantized interband transitions, which, when analyzed, provide information

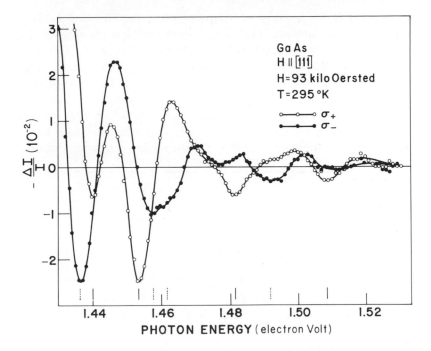

FIGURE 8. Cross-field magneto-absorption in gallium arsenide. Sigma plus and sigma minus refer to positive and negative circularly polarized waves. (After Vrehen, ref. 28).

about energy band parameters for holes and electrons. This has been done successfully in germanium first, and now many of the compound semiconductors are succumbing to improved techniques with high magnetic fields. These new techniques include such exotic phenomena which go by the name of photon-assisted magneto-tunneling and magneto-emission. The latter have been studied by observing the radiation emitted by diodes, lasers, and optically excited semiconductors. These observations complement the absorption and reflection experiments. In order to exploit this new quantum magneto-optical phenomenon in metals, it was evident that transmission or absorption experiments on single crystals were impractical. Consequently, a magneto-reflection technique was innovated. This was highly successful in bismuth[29] where the infrared energy was fixed in a wavelength and the magnetic field was swept to the highest fields possible for a range of frequencies in the infrared between ten and twenty microns. The results were rather surprising in that no effect was observed, except with the magnetic field. The trace shown in Fig. 9 is typical for one of two crystal orientations. When these oscillatory data are collated and plotted as a function of fields versus energy, a fan shaped pattern of points results. Upon developing a theoretical model of the energy bands in which three important parameters, namely an energy gap, an effective mass at the bottom of the conduction band and a spin value are predicted, then

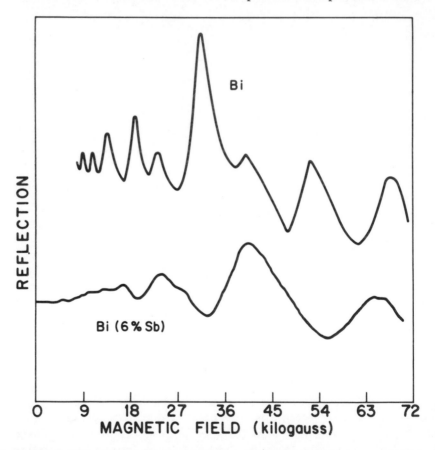

FIGURE 9. Magnetoreflection in bismuth and bismuth-antimony alloy showing two sets of interband transitions as indicated by the reflection peaks. (After Brown, Mavroides, and Lax, ref. 29).

the theoretical curves fit the data as shown in Fig. 10. The remarkable feature of this experiment is that it also permits the determination of the Fermi energy, the anistrophy of the energy bands, and most important, from the fit of the data to a model of the bands not only at the Fermi surface, but above and below it, an energy gap is determined. This spectacular approach has recently been duplicated and applied elegantly to an even more complex system in graphite[30]

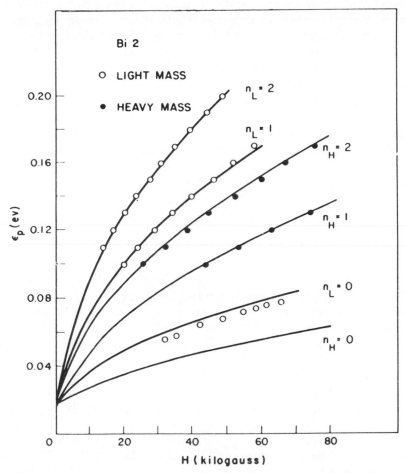

FIGURE 10. Correlation of theory and experiment of magnetoreflection in bismuth. Solid lines are theoretical lines and points are experimental. (After Brown, Mavroides and Lax, ref 29).

in which seven parameters are necessary to specify the energy structure of this well known, but until now poorly understood, semimetal. The magnetoreflection experiments at fields of 100 kilogauss in pyrolytic graphite are capable of evaluating the pertinent parameters to three significant figures and firmly establish the theoretical model of the bands in a most convincing manner. The Fermi surface deduced from these data for holes and electrons exhibits the unexpected shape of a rocket as shown in Fig. 11. Following graphite, other semimetals such as antimony[31] and the compound mercurytelluride have recently succumbed to the above technique. The results already have demonstrated that the energy bands of these materials are quite different than that predicted on the basis of intraband measurements such as de Haas-van Alphen effect, magnetoresistance, and cyclotron resonance. This should not be surprising since the interband magneto-optical effects with polarized light and related selection rules provide more information about the symmetry properties of these energy states and over a wider range of energies. Ultimately, when further refined in sensitivity, this technique should prove to be a powerful tool for studying the energy structure in an increasing number of metals.

D. OSCILLATORY EFFECTS

The first evidence of the quantization of levels in metals in a magnetic field were the observation of oscillations in the magnetoresistance of bismuth, which has been called the Shubnikov-de Haas effect. A related phenomenon in which the magnetic susceptibility was observed to oscillate at low temperatures is known as the de Haas-van Alphen effect. The latter, which has been studied as a function of temperature in the liquid helium range, exhibits oscillations due to the coincidence of the magnetic levels with the Fermi energy. As the magnetic field is increased, different quantum levels associated with the coalescence of the energy states successively reach the energy of the Fermi level resulting first in an enhanced population of electrons at the coincident level and a decrease when this magnetic level exceeds the Fermi energy. From the study of this periodic variation as a function of magnetic field, crystal orientation and temperature, a great deal of information regarding metals has been derived, both with high dc fields and large pulsed magnetic fields.[32] The de Haas-van Alphen or Shubnikov-de Haas oscillations as they are called can, of course, be observed by a number of other techniques besides the magnetic susceptibility and magnetoresistance. Very recently it has been observed in the infrared reflection from antimony near the plasma edge. But perhaps the most important technique that has evolved is the ultrasonic attenuation in

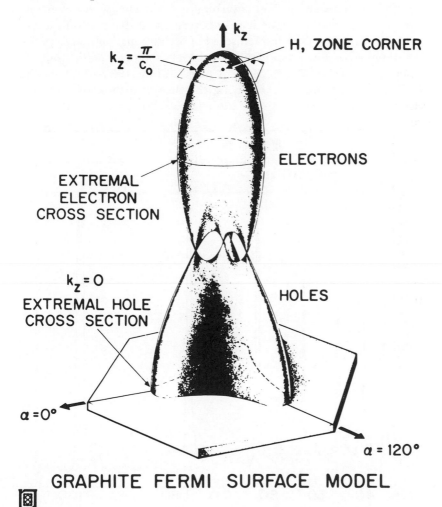

GRAPHITE FERMI SURFACE MODEL

FIGURE 11. Sketch of the Fermi surface of graphite obtained from magnetoreflection experiments. (After Dresselhaus and Mavroides, ref. 30).

metals, which not only shows these quantum oscillations, but a number of other equally important quantum and geometrical phenomena.[33] One of the most striking examples of this is known as the giant quantum oscillations.[34] This was predicted theoretically on the basis that those electrons which travel at the velocity of sound parallel to the magnetic field absorb most of the energy in the metal. Consequently, as the magnetic field is varied and the quantum levels coincide with the Fermi level, instead of oscillations, very large peaks are observed at low temperatures and high magnetic fields. Indeed, when this experiment was performed in gallium, the pattern shown in Fig. 12 was found.[35] In applying the theory to these data, it was possible to determine not only the effective mass, but also the spin

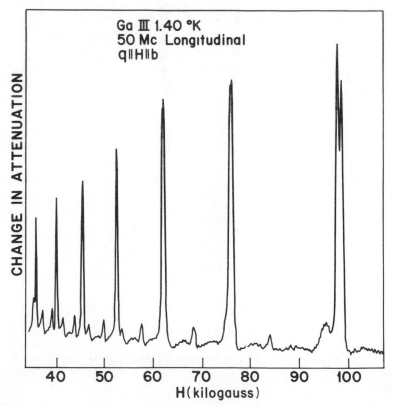

FIGURE 12. Giant quantum oscillations in gallium obtained from ultrasonic attenuation in a magnetic field. (After Shapira and Lax, ref. 35).

factor for the first time from observations of the splitting of the peaks above 100 kilogauss. Furthermore, a deformation potential, i. e., the coupling of the electrons with the lattice, and the relaxation time were also estimated. The ultrasonic techniques are also important in determining the size and shape of the Fermi surface.

III. CONCLUSIONS

It is difficult in a short discourse such as this to adequately cover the extent and full scope of high magnetic field research that has evolved during the last decade. The activity and productivity has far exceeded the expectations of even its most ardent participants. Only a few years ago such phenomena as the Mössbauer effect, coherent radiation with lasers, and high field superconductivity did not exist. But each of these now has become a prominent area of research which will play an important future role under the heading of high magnetic fields. However, there are many which we have not mentioned which promise to enrich this field of science even further. For example, there is a host of possibilities involving electron beams in magnetic fields which will be extremely interesting as sources for radiation in the millimeter and far infrared. A synchrotron radiation source in high magnetic fields is capable of developing into a broad band incoherent radiation source from the microwave to the far ultraviolet, which when properly designed, can exceed present sources in the energy-starved regions of the electromagnetic spectrum by two to four orders of magnitude. The possibility of putting high pressure equipment into the existing large volume high field water-cooled magnets will permit the examination of the electrical, optical, and magnetic properties of a whole new host of crystals which experience phase transformation at these ultra-high pressures. Thus our knowledge of the basic properties of these materials and their dependence on their atomic configuration can be tremendously enhanced. These are only a few examples of future developments. However, it can be said that in science, whenever the tools are extended quantitatively to the limit allowed by nature and human ingenuity and at least one order of magnitude beyond that which the state-of-the-art has previously reached, then inevitably new phenomena are discovered and new knowledge about the science of materials always is developed. In high magnetic field research we have cascaded these new techniques and succeeded in combining the extreme values of the physical parameters such as low temperatures, high fields, high purity of crystals, high resolution spectroscopy, extreme ranges of frequency, and now high pressures. This combination of techniques when carried to its ultimate, plus experimental ingenuity and more sophisticated theoretical analysis abetted by modern computer processing, presents an exciting program of fruitful research with high magnetic fields that will engage a great many physicists and engineers very profitably in this exciting area of research for the next generation at least.

REFERENCES

[1] H. Deslandres and A. Perot, *Comptes Rendus 159*, 438 (1914).

[2] P. L. Kapitza, *Proc. Roy. Soc. A105*, 691 (1924); *A115*, 658 (1927).

[3] F. Bitter, *Rev. Sci. Inst. 7*, 479 (1936); *7*, 482 (1936); *8*, 318 (1937); *10*, 373 (1939).

[4] H. P. Furth and R. W. Waniek, *Rev. Sci. Inst. 27*, 195 (1956).

[5] S. Foner and H. H. Kolm, *Rev. Sci. Inst. 27*, 547 (1956).

[6] H. P. Furth, R. W. Waniek and M. A. Levine, *Rev. Sci. Inst. 28*, 949 (1957).

[7] C. M. Fowler, R. S. Caird, W. B. Garn and D. B. Thompson, *High Magnetic Fields*, MIT Press, Cambridge, Mass., 1962, p. 269.

[8] *Physics Today 15*, 82 (Sept. 1962).

[9] For more detail see F. Bitter, *British J. of Appl. Physics 14*, 579 (1963).

[10] D. B. Montgomery, *Prog. Phys. 26*, 69 (1963).

[11] W. J. De Haas and J. B. Westerdijk, *Nature 158*, 271 (1946); H. Zijlstra, *High Magnetic Fields*, MIT Press, Cambridge, Mass. 1962, p. 281.

[12] H. L. Laquer, *High Magnetic Fields*, MIT Press, Cambridge, Mass. 1962, p. 156.

[13] J. R. Purcell, *Ibid.*, p. 166.

[14] J. C. Laurence and G. V. Brown, *Ibid.*, p. 170.

[15] H. Kamerlingh-Onnes, *Leiden Comm.* No. 133d (1913).

[16] S. H. Autler, *Rev. Sci. Inst., 31*, 369 (1960).

[17] J. E. Kunzler, E. Buehler, F. S. L. Hsu, B. T. Matthias and C. Wahl, *J. Appl. Phys. 32*, 325 (1961); J. E. Junzler, E. Buehler, F. S. L. Hsu and J. H. Wernick, *Phys. Rev. Letters 6*, 89 (1961).

[18] General Electric *Cryostrand Newsletter*, Feb. 1965; *Metals. Rev. 38*, No. 5, 1965, p. 15.

[19] *Physics Today 18*, 81 (Jan. 1965).

[20] Adapted from Hulm, Chandrasekhar and Riemersma, *Int. Sci. and Tech. 17*, 50 (May 1963).

[21] D. B. Montgomery, *NEREM Record*, Boston Section IEEE, *6*, 179 (1964).

[22] B. Lax and J. G. Mavroides, *Solid State Physics, Advances in Research and Applications*, Vol. II, Academic Press, New York (1960) p. 261.

[23] G. B. Wright and B. Lax, *J. Appl. Physics 32*, 2113 (1961).

[24] P. Aigrain, *Proceedings of the Int. Conf. on Semiconductor Physics*, Prague 1960, Pub. House of Czech. Acad. of Sciences, Prague (1961) p. 224.

[25] J. K. Furdyna, *Phys. Rev. Letters 14,* 635 (1965).

[26] S. J. Buchsbaum and J. K. Galt, *Phys. Fluids, 4,* 1514 (1961).

[27] B. Lax and J. G. Mavroides, to be published in *Semiconductors and Semimetals,* Ed. by R. K. Willardson and A. C. Beer.

[28] Q. Vrehen, *Bull. Am. Phys. Soc. 10,* 534 (1965).

[29] R. N. Brown, J. G. Mavroides and B. Lax, *Phys. Rev. 129,* 2055 (1963).

[30] M. S. Dresselhaus and J. G. Mavroides, IBM *J. of Research and Development 8,* 262 (1964).

[31] M. S. Dresselhaus and J. G. Mavroides, *Phys. Rev. Letters, 14,* 259 (1965).

[32] D. Shoenberg, *Progress in Low Temperature Physics,* Vol. 11, Ed. C. J. Gorter, North Holland, Amsterdam (1957) p. 226.

[33] R. W. Morse, *Progress in Cryogenics,* Vol. I. Ed. Mendelssohn Heywood (1959).

[34] V. L. Gurevich, V. G. Skobov and Y. A. Fivsov, *Soviet Physics,* JETP *13,* 552 (1961).

[35] Y. Shapira and B. Lax, *Phys. Rev. 138,* A1191 (1965).

XIII. The Relation of ATR to Absorption Spectra in the Infrared

BRYCE CRAWFORD, JR.

FOR OVER A quarter of a century chemists have used infrared spectroscopy as a diagnostic and analytical tool in the characterization of materials. In this application the absorption spectrum of the sample between 400 and 4000 cm^{-1} is determined; its qualitative appearance, more specifically the appearance of characteristic absorption bands at certain "group frequencies," has enabled the chemist to identify the material qualitatively,[1] and the quantitative measurement of the absorbance of the sample has permitted him to determine the amounts of the components in a mixture.[2] A few years ago the similar use of the "Attenuated Total Reflection" (ATR) spectrum was described by Fahrenfort[3] and since his paper the method has received considerable attention from chemists and from instrument makers. The claim usually advanced is that the ATR technique is more convenient for certain types of samples, and that in these cases the chemist can, by properly using ATR, obtain a spectrum "essentially identical" to the absorption spectrum, which he can then use in the familiar fashion. Our purpose in this paper is not to enter into the discussion of the relative conveniences of ATR and absorption spectra for various sample situations, but to present a qualitative treatment of the factors which control the appearance of ATR spectra. With an understanding of these factors, we can understand and even interpret the very real differences between ATR and conventional absorption spectra, and hence choose experimental conditions which produce ATR spectra most suitable for a particular application.

BRYCE CRAWFORD, Jr. is Dean of the Graduate School and Professor of Physical Chemistry at the University of Minnesota. His researches have been in basic scientific kinetics of flames and propellants, with his interests centering on molecular spectroscopy and molecular structure.

The Nature of the ATR Spectrum

To obtain an ATR spectrum, we measure the attenuation of a beam of infrared light reflected internally from the surface of some transparent optically-dense material which is in good optical contact with the sample. The light penetrates only a few microns into the sample, so that its thickness beyond the first few microns does not matter. We shall not describe the various optical systems which have been used in ATR spectroscopy as the details can be found elsewhere, e.g. in Fahrenfort's original paper.[3] The essential optical path, which we shall presently discuss, is shown in Figure 1.

We can regard an ATR spectrum either as a substitute for a conventional absorption spectrum or as a distinct optical observation

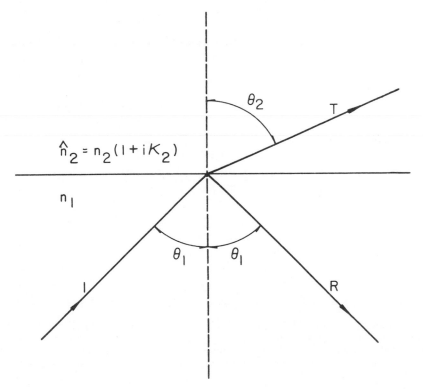

Figure 1. Optical path of light rays at an interface.

yielding certain information. If we view it as *a substitute for an absorption spectrum,* we note;

(a) sampling may be easier in certain cases;

(b) the optical system is more complex;

(c) the bands are "distorted" in comparison with absorption bands, though the distortion can be controlled and minimized;

(d) the relative band intensities are changed.

If we view it as *a distinct optical observation,* we note:

(a) both the refractive index and the absorption coefficient of the sample may be determined;

(b) only the surface layers of the sample are observed;

(c) the depth of penetration can be controlled;

(d) the light beam is nearly parallel and of small area where it interacts with the sample, providing a convenient situation to use polarized light in the study of anisotropic samples.

The primary reason for differences between ATR and absorption spectra lies in the effect of the sample refractive index. The conventional absorption spectrum is sensitive to changes in the absorption coefficient of the sample, but essentially independent of changes in the refractive index. Both these factors are important in ATR observations, and in the neighborhood of an absorption band both these factors change very markedly with frequency. In the following we shall consider the basic optical situation and discuss in detail the way in which quite different spectral appearances may arise. We shall focus our discussion on isotropic samples.

Basic Optical Theory

Consider (Figure 1.) a ray of infrared light, I, incident on a boundary between a transparent material with a high refractive index n_1, and the sample with refractive index n_2. At a frequency where the sample does not absorb, consider the effect on reflectivity, defined as the intensity-ratio R/I, of increasing the angle θ_1.* At first, at low

---

* Ideally the incident light should be parallel so that all the rays in the beam have the same angle of incidence, θ_1. In practice this ideal can be approached by making medium 1 in the form of a hemicylinder or, if n_1 is very high (e.g., germanium, $n_1 = 4$), by simply focusing the convergent beam onto a flat external absorbing sample provides an excellent test of angle resolution. The rounding of the curve near the critical angle, by comparison with the theoretical curve for parallel light (see Fig. 2), is a measure of the nonparallelism of the incident light.

θ_1, the energy of the incident light is divided into a reflected and a transmitted ray. The angles and refractive indices are related by Snell's Law:

$$n_1 \sin \theta_1 = n_2 \sin \theta_2 \qquad (1)$$

If $n_1 > n_2$, a value of θ_1 is reached when the transmitted ray is grazing the boundary. This is the critical angle, θ_c, and the light is totally internally reflected for all larger values of θ_1. This is illustrated in Fig. 2. The critical angle is obtained from $n_1 \sin \theta_c = n_2$

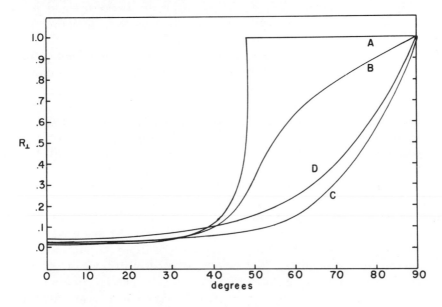

FIGURE 2. "Angle-scan" curves: reflectivity against angle of incidence. All curves assume $n_2 = 1.45$. For internal reflection, curves A and B, $n_1 = 1.95$; for A, $n_2\kappa_2 = 0$, for B, $n_2\kappa_2 = 0.35$. For external reflection, curves C and D, $n_1 = 1.0$; for C, $n_2\kappa_2 = 0$, for D, $n_2\kappa_2 = 0.35$.

and the following two inequalities, modified by the effect of absorption as described in the next section will prove to be very useful:

NON-TOTAL REFLECTION: $\qquad n_1 \sin \theta_1 < n_2$

$$\qquad (2)$$

TOTAL REFLECTION: $\qquad n_1 \sin \theta_1 > n_2$

When the light is totally reflected there is still an electromagnetic wave on the sample side of the boundary. This phenomenon is well known and has been discussed clearly in Born and Wolf[4] and Jenkins and White.[5] The important points are as follows:

1) The wave in the sample is not a simple transverse wave such as the incident or reflected waves. Theory shows that its amplitude, which falls off exponentially with distance away from the boundary, depends on the values of n_1, n_2 and θ_1 such that it is strongest just above the critical angle and zero at grazing incidence ($\theta_1 = 90°$).

2) There is an instantaneous flow of energy backward and forward across the boundary but (for a transparent sample) no net transfer of energy into the sample.

3) There is a net transfer of energy through the sample along the boundary parallel to the plane of incidence. The distance traveled in the sample before recrossing the boundary also depends on n_1, n_2, and θ_1 and is greatest just above the critical angle and zero at grazing incidence.

So far we have assumed that the sample is transparent. We now consider the more general case when this is not so. At a frequency where the sample absorbs light the refractive index becomes a complex quantity and is written $\hat{n}_2$. It is made up of a real and an imaginary part: $\hat{n}_2 = n_2(1 + i\ \kappa_2)$ where $i = \sqrt{-1}$. We shall consider the real part, n_2, to be the same as the n_2 above. This is not strictly correct when the sample absorbs and the refracted angle θ_2 is no longer given by Snell's Law as stated in equation (1). However, if we continue to define a critical angle by equations (2) we can give a good qualitative account of ATR band shapes. The imaginary part, $n_2\kappa_2$, is a measure of the rate at which light passing through the sample is attenuated. We call $\hat{n}_2$ the complex refractive index, n_2 the refractive index, $n_2\kappa_2$ the extinction coefficient and κ_2 the attenuation index of the sample. n_2 and $n_2\kappa_2$ are referred to collectively as the "optical constants." The extinction coefficient is related to the absorption coefficient, a, of the Bouguer-Lambert Law ($I/I_o = e^{-ax}$) by $4\pi\nu\ n_2\ \kappa_2 = a$, where ν is the vacuum wavenumber of the radiation. At angles below θ_c, the reflectivity is less than 1 since a transmitted ray exists; absorption by the sample modifies the reflectivity only slightly until θ_1 approaches θ_c, because energy in the reflected beam has interacted strongly with the sample, some of the energy will be trapped if the sample absorbs. The reflected beam is then attenuated and, because the amplitude of the light wave and the distance it travels through the sample are greatest when θ_1 is just above the critical angle, the attenuation for a given absorption coefficient will be greatest at this angle of incidence. The attenuation decreases to zero at grazing incidence.

In Figure 2, curves A and B show the reflectivity as a function of the angle θ_1 for a transparent and an absorbing sample respectively, against an optically-dense medium ($n_1 = 1.95$), assuming a reasonable sample refractive index ($n_2 = 1.45$); a moderately high extinction coefficient ($n_2\kappa_2 = 0.35$) has been assumed for the absorbing case. The attenuation which will be observed at a given setting of θ_1 is of course the vertical difference between curve A and curve B at that angle. The curves will be different for every combination of n_1, n_2, and $n_2\kappa_2$, but the general features of this example will appear in any case. The trends outlined in the last few paragraphs are well illustrated, and these curves will repay thoughtful study. They show in particular that the attenuation due to the extinction coefficient is greatest at angles just above the critical angle θ_c; this then is the region of angle setting where the ATR technique has greatest sensitivity to sample absorption. It is also the angle range where the curve is steepest against angle, and hence where any error in angle setting will have the greatest effect; quantitative study shows that, for real accuracy in measurement of the attenuation, the angle should be reproducible at least to 0.1 degree. The curves show also that, as the angle setting moves up higher than θ_c, the attenuation becomes less.

The curves in Figure 2 have been calculated for the optically simplest case, that of polarized light perpendicular to the plane of incidence at the sample surface. The opposite-polarization curves are qualitatively similar. We shall not consider in this paper the polarization effects, since our qualitative arguments are valid for both polarizations. But it should be noted that the effects of polarization are quantitatively quite noticeable. This can be used to good advantage in studying anisotropic or oriented samples by ATR, as has been mentioned. It can also be regarded as a disadvantage in that ATR observations are affected by the polarization discrimination, or greater efficiency for one polarization than for the other, and in the case of grating spectrometers this discrimination can be quite significant.

Curves C and D in Figure 2 show the reflectivities for the same pair of samples, transparent and absorbing, when they are examined by conventional or external reflection methods; i.e., when there is no optically-dense medium involved, and the refractive index n_1 is simply that of air, $n_1 = 1.0$. It will be noted that the use of internal total reflection both increases the reflected intensity so that we have more light to work with, and increases the effect of the sample absorption, the attenuation.

BAND SHAPES AND INTENSITIES IN ATR SPECTRA

If we proceed to examine the course of a spectral run, in which a given angle setting is used and the observed reflectivity is plotted against the frequency of the light being reflected, we must take into account the fact that the sample refractive index n_2 strongly affects the critical angle and hence the reflectivity. It is a general law of nature that the refractive index of a substance varies rapidly in the neighborhood of an absorption band: wherever the extinction coefficient $n_2\kappa_2$ goes through a maximum (an absorption peak) there is an oscillation in the curve of n_2 against frequency, with a region of anomalous dispersion across the band center. This behaviour can be understood if we consider the molecules of the sample as damped oscillators set in motion by the oscillating electrical field of the light wave, having a resonant frequency equal to the light frequency at the absorption peak; more sophisticated and more accurate models such as the Lorentz or the Van-Vleck-Weisskopf model show the same qualitative behavior. We may discuss the effects in connection with a specific example: Figure 3 shows the course of the two optical constants n_2 and $n_2\kappa_2$ for liquid benzene in the region of the 675 cm^{-1} band.

A. DEPENDENCE ON n_1 AND θ_1.

If now we choose a given optically-dense material, thus fixing n_1, and also choose a given setting θ_1, we shall fix the value of $n_1\sin\theta_1$; wherever this is greater than n_2 the condition for total reflection is satisfied as noted in equations (2), and we may proceed to ask whether the value of $n_2\kappa_2$ is significant so that attenuation may occur. Three choices of these instrumental parameters are indicated in Figure 3, and the resulting ATR spectra shown in Figure 4. We have taken n_1 as 2.37, the value for KRS-5, which is the most popular

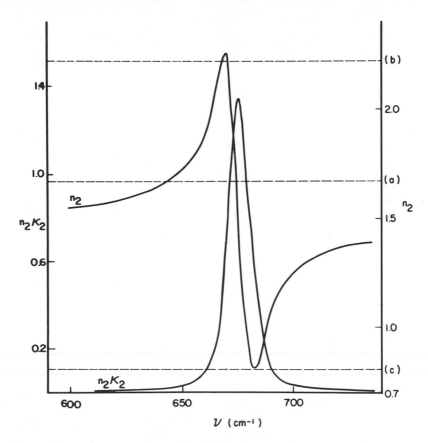

FIGURE 3. Optical constants of liquid benzene in the region of 675 cm⁻¹. Broken lines indicate conditions described in the text.

ATR material, and have considered three angles, (a) 45°, (b) 70°, and (c) 20°. The broken lines in Figure 3 mark the value of n_1 sin θ_1 for these three choices.

(a) Let us consider the case of the 45° setting and trace the behavior of the reflectivity from higher toward lower frequencies, considering at each point first the relative values of n_1 sin θ_1 and n_2, and then the value of the extinction coefficient $n_2\kappa_2$. At 725 cm⁻¹ on the wing of the band $n_2\kappa_2$ is negligible and n_1 sin $\theta_1 > n_2$ so that the reflectivity is 1. At 700 cm⁻¹ the sample starts to absorp and the beam is attenuated. Between 700 and 680 cm⁻¹ the attenuation increases as

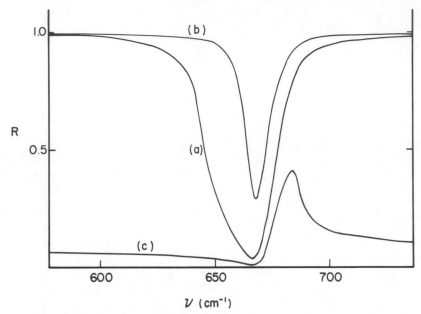

FIGURE 4. ATR spectra for liquid benzene in the 675 cm^{-1} region, using KRS-5 at an angle of incidence of (a) 45°, (b) 70°, and (c) 20°.

the absorption coefficient increases. Thus far the ATR band resembles closely the absorption band. At 675cm^{-1} the absorption coefficient starts to decrease but n_2 is increasing rapidly and a point is reached where n_2 becomes greater than $n_1 \sin \theta_1$, so that total reflection no longer occurs. Energy is now lost to a transmitted beam and the ATR band is broadened on the low-frequency side by comparison with the absorption band. At lower frequencies, the absorption becomes negligible and $n_1 \sin \theta_1$ exceeds n_2 so that total reflection occurs once more. The broadening on the low frequency side produces a shift to lower frequency of the peak of the ATR band compared with the peak of the absorption band. This shift can be quite considerable.

(b) To reduce the distortion of situation (a) we need to ensure that $n_1 \sin \theta_1 > n_2$ for all frequencies. This we do by choosing a higher angle, 70°. A more detailed study shows that the distortion decreases the larger we make $n_1 \sin \theta_1$ but is never entirely absent. However, as $n_1 \sin \theta_1$ is increased, both the amplitude of the light wave in the sample and the length of its travel through the sample are decreased and so the overall attenuation is less.

(c) Grossly distorted bands are easily obtained by choosing a low value of $n_1 \sin \theta_1$. In the case of a 20° angle $n_1 \sin \theta_1 < n_2$ over most of the band. The highest reflectivity is when $n_1 \sin \theta_1$ approaches n_2 but here the sample has appreciable absorption and so the reflectivity is never total.

These examples show that we have to make a compromise between strong bands which are distorted and relatively undistorted bands which are weak. If our aim is to produce ATR spectra resembling absorption spectra, we will be drawn to the second alternative; if the attenuation is then too weak, we can produce a stronger band by summing the attenuation at a number of successive reflections with a multiple-reflection apparatus. This is analogous to increasing the thickness of an absorption cell an integral number of times. It is important to realize that multiple reflections at high $n_1 \sin \theta_1$ produce an intense band which is much more symmetrical than the same-strength band obtained with one reflection at low $n_1 \sin \theta_1$.

B.   DEPENDENCE OF ATTENUATION ON FREQUENCY

Assuming we have chosen $n_1 \sin \theta_1 > n_2$ over the whole spectrum the attenuation of an ATR band is primarily dependent on $n_2\kappa_2$, which as noted before is proportional to the a of the Bouguer-Lambert Law divided by the wavenumber. Consequently, in comparison with an absorption spectrum, an ATR spectrum shows relatively weak high-frequency bands and relatively strong low-frequency bands. This is a large effect since the wavenumber can change by a factor of ten over the range of an infrared spectrum.

C.   INTERACTION BETWEEN NEIGHBORING BANDS

The relative intensity of two strong, neighboring bands is often considerably changed in an ATR spectrum. This is quite apart from effect B and is due to n_2. The curve of n_2 versus frequency is the sum of two closely-spaced oscillations. The result gives a relatively higher value of n_2 through the region of the lower-frequency band and so the lower-frequency band will appear relatively more intense by ATR. The effect is minimized by choosing a high value of $n_1 \sin \theta_1$. A particularly striking but not unique example of this exists in the ATR spectrum of liquid carbon tetrachloride where the two components of the Fermi doublet at 770 cm^{-1} have their relative intensities reversed.

D. SOLVENT REFRACTIVE INDEX

In a solution the n_2 which is important is that of the solution as a whole. Thus if a solute is dissolved in a transparent solvent of high refractive index, the ATR bands will appear relatively stronger and more distorted for a given value of $n_1 \sin \theta_1$ than if the refractive index of the solvent had been low. Therefore, in the case of solutions we can exercise a further degree of control over the form of the spectrum by our choice of solvent refractive index.

E. EFFECT OF SOLVENT ABSORPTION BANDS

This is analogous to effect C. A good example is a series of mixtures of carbon disulphide and acetone. The very strong CS_2 absorption at 1510 cm^{-1} falls between three weaker acetone bands at 1720, 1370, and 1240 cm^{-1}. As the CS_2 concentration is increased, the value of n_2 of the solution is raised on the low-frequency side of the CS_2 band relative to that on the high-frequency side. This causes the two low-frequency acetone bands to gain in apparent intensity (and in distortion) at the expense of the high-frequency band.

F. EFFECT OF IMPERFECT OPTICAL CONTACT

So far we have assumed perfect optical contact between the optically-dense medium and the sample. This is no problem, of course, with liquid samples but can be quite a real difficulty with crystals or rigid materials. Various techniques ranging from the optical polishing of a single-crystal sample to the use of pressure to press a reasonably pliable sample against the ATR optically-dense element can be used. The qualitative effect of areas of poor contact is easy to understand; in such areas n_2 will be that of air, namely 1.0, and total reflection, unattenuated, will occur. The result will, of course, be simply to weaken the attenuation as recorded on the ATR spectrum: a quite tolerable phenomenon as long as the weakening is not too serious, and as long as quantitative observations are not being attempted.

It is at least not difficult to observe the extent of poor contact, providing that the ATR element is transparent in the visible region as is the case with KRS-5. One can observe the reflection of visible light with the eye, choosing an angle of observation such that the total-reflection condition (2) is satisfied for the air-element interface but not for the sample-element interface; then the areas of poor optical contact (the air-element interface areas) will appear bright against the dark areas of good optical contact.

It should be noted that the use of liquids such as mineral oil to promote optical contact has its own dangers. The mineral oil will have an intermediate refractive index and will promote passage of the light into the sample; but such oils naturally have their own absorption bands, and the resulting spectrum will be affected by these bands, as well as by the rather complicated situation involving three layers of different refractive indices all within the depth of penetration of the light.

QUANTITATIVE STUDIES USING ATR

It is possible to use ATR to obtain precise values of both optical constants of a sample by making measurements at two angles of incidence. Using the appropriate equations, both n_2 and $n_2\kappa_2$ may be obtained. The calculations are, however, fairly sophisticated and lengthy, and are scarcely practical if the object is simply quantitative analysis to determine the concentration of solute B in solvent A.

A detailed discussion of the quantitative relation between R, the observed reflectivity, and the properties of the sample is beyond the scope of this paper. We note, however, that Beer's Law *does not apply*, and no simple general relation between the observed R and the absorbance of the sample is available. Indeed, our discussion to this point has made clear that the value of R depends not only on $n_2\kappa_2$ but also on n_2, on n_1, and on θ_1. It would appear possible to devise empirical "calibration curves" for practical samples *if* the values of these last three constants can in fact be held constant from one run to another. This is easy for n_1, and not too difficult for θ_1, if the ATR spectrometer is mechanically constructed to provide a precise and reproducible angle setting, but the variation of the sample refractive index n_2 would seem to be more difficult. Under some conditions one may expect the relation between the observed R and the extinction coefficient to take a comfortable form; Flournoy has given some results along this line. [6]

ACKNOWLEDGMENTS

The considerations and examples given here were worked out in collaboration with A. C. Gilby and John Burr in the course of a research program on infrared intensity measurements.

REFERENCES

[1] L. J. Bellamy, *Infrared Spectrum of Complex Molecules*, 2nd edition, Wiley, New York, 1958.

[2] W. J. Potts, Jr., *Chemical Infrared Spectroscopy, Vol. I*, Wiley, New York, 1963.

[3] J. Fahrenfort, *Spectrochemica Acta, 17*, 698 (1961).

J. Fahrenfort & W. M. Visser, *Ibid, 18*, 1103 (1962).

[4] Born & Wolf, *Principles of Optics*, Pergamon Press, 1959.

[5] Jenkins & White, *Fundamentals of Optics*, 2nd edition, McGraw-Hill, New York, 1950.

[6] P. A. Flournoy, *Journal of Chemical Physics, 39*, 3156 (1963).

XIV. Space Chemistry

Willard F. Libby

Space chemistry is, in our definition, chemistry under the unusual conditions of outer space and inner space. Our sheltered environment here on the earth has led to an overemphasis on the chemistry peculiar to our conditions. Our program in chemistry at UCLA is aimed to work in those areas which are different from the normal environmental conditions. Thus we work in these areas: high pressure chemistry, radiation chemistry, high temperature chemistry, and vacuum chemistry. So far we have made progress only in the first two areas, although we have a substantial beginning in the way of apparatus for the third area. But our program in Space Chemistry is aimed at these four general areas: high pressure, radiation, high temperature, and vacuum. Our research has been most generously supported by the Directorate of Chemical Sciences of the Air Force Office of Scientific Research. We are extremely grateful for this support.

I HIGH PRESSURE CHEMISTRY

Our work in the chemistry of high pressures has been possible only because of the collaboration of our colleagues expert in the techniques of high pressure; Professor George C. Kennedy and Professor David Griggs of the Institute of Geophysics, both of whom learned their high pressure work from Percy Bridgman at Harvard. In addition, we have been greatly assisted by Professor Harry Drickamer at the University of Illinois, and Professor Tracy Hall of Brigham Young University. In other words, our objective has been to apply to chemistry the techniques that have been gained by the Bridgman school and others to bring out the effects of high pressures on chem-

WILLARD F. LIBBY, Professor of Chemistry at the University of California, Los Angeles. Director of the University of California Institute of Geophysics and Planetary Physics, and a former member of the Atomic Energy Commission. He is a Nobel Laureate (1960, chemistry, carbon-14 method), and is an AFOSR grantee. He directs the AFOSR Program in Space Chemistry at UCLA.

ical reactions and chemical properties. There have been two general areas: the organic, and the inorganic.

A.   ORGANIC HIGH PRESSURE CHEMISTRY

1.   *Virus Killing*—Our work in organic compounds consists mainly of the study of the effects of high pressure on Coliphage T-4; work done mainly by Lewis Solomon, Peter Zeegen, and Fred Eiserling. Coliphage T-4 virus was exposed to pressures of 4 kb under which condition it was found to be rapidly inactivated by the release of deoxyribonucleic acid (DNA) and the uncoiling of this important molecule. Electronmicroscopic pictures indicated the pressure consistently caused two morphological changes; both attributed to the uncoiling: (1) the phage with contracted sheaths and heads full of DNA, and (2) the phage with contracted sheaths and heads empty of DNA. The ratios of the types have been shown to depend strongly on temperature. Bioassays of the results of phage samples check with the counts made and the electronmicroscopic pictures.

The fraction of the initial phage population surviving exposure to pressures on the order of 4 kb. was found to increase following the addition of ions, chloroform, or protein to the phosphate-buffered stock suspension. It has not been determined whether these compositional variables act through direct interaction with the phage or by altering the organization of the water.[1]

The significant features of the kinetic studies are 1) the linearity of the log fraction surviving-time curves and 2) the failure of such curves to extrapolate to initial concentration at time zero. Linearity was contingent upon the initial phage concentration being on the order of 10^{10}/ml or less. It was not determined if exposure times longer than five minutes would cause a deviation from linearity for these stocks. The rapid inactivation made it difficult to determine whether initial first order kinetics is lost at pressures greater than 3.4 g.u. (1 gauge unit is approximately 1.4 kilobars).

Compression and decompression appear to have an inactivating effect which cannot be accounted for by accumulative inactivation due to the finite time spent at each pressure during compression and decompression. An upper limit to the fraction of phage inactivated during compression and decompression by the mechanism which inactivates phage at constant pressure can be obtained. Assuming inactivation is first order, $\dfrac{d \ (\log \text{ surviving fraction})}{dt} = -.43K$ where K is the pressure dependent inactivation constant and .43 the factor for logarithm change of base. Since compression and decompression rates are constant, $dp/dt = 2.0$ g.u./min., and log fraction surviving compression $= {}_0\!\int^{3.1} .43K \ (dp/2)$.

This integral can be estimated by taking .43/2 times the area under the rate constant-pressure curve in Figure 1. Doubling this

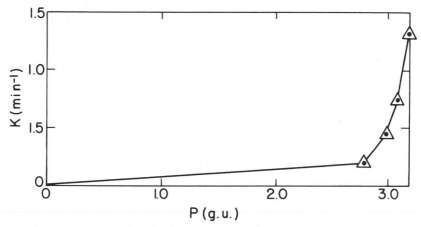

FIGURE 1. First order inactivation constant vs. pressure. The initial viable titer was 1.1×10^{10}/ml. Phage were compressed and decompressed at 1 g.u./min. Temperature was 25°C.

value to account for decompression gives .23 or 41% lost due to compression and decompression. This estimate falls considerably short of the 75% inactivation obtained by extrapolation, so it is likely that changing pressures can have an additional inactivating effect.

Electron micrographs show two phage types which can be considered inactive from their morphology—those with contracted sheaths and those with both empty heads and contracted sheaths. Electron micrographs of compressed samples have also shown a large number of free tail fibers. Thus, pressure may provide a practical method of isolating tail fiber protein.

The mechanism of contraction and DNA release remains obscure. Osmotic mechanisms, however, based on pressure differentially altering the permeability of soluble ions and water across the phage coat is not likely, since preliminary results indicate that osmotic shock resistant mutants show the same degree of inactivation as the wild type. No evidence has been obtained which would indicate whether the two morphological types arise from two separate reac-

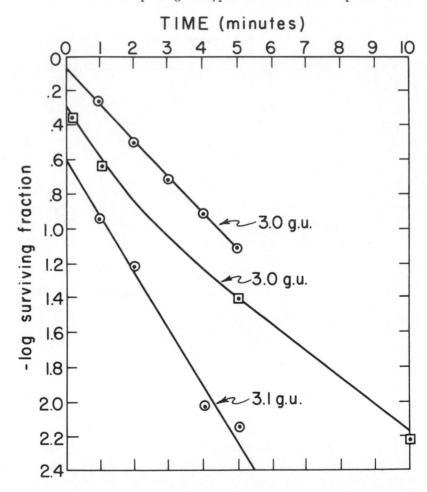

FIGURE 2. Negative log surviving fraction vs. time. Time is measured between the end of compression and the beginning of decompression. Compression and decompression rate is 2 g.u./min. Temperature was 25°C. Initial viable titer 5 x 10[9]/ml. Initial viable titer 5 x 10[11]/ml. Pressure 3.0 g.u. Figure 4 is an electron micrograph of these phage after 5 minutes.

tions or if the empty headed phage with contracted sheath is formed from full headed phage with contracted sheath upon loss of DNA.

Furthermore, morphological alteration may be secondary to a primary nonvisible inactivating step.

Variation of temperature has been shown to alter the ratio of the two morphologically altered types. Especially noteworthy is the effect temperature has on the ratio of full to empty headed phage among those with contracted sheaths. There is a marked decrease in the emptying of DNA at lower temperatures. This observation may have more general utility since it indicates that the temperature variable may be useful when it is desirable to favor one pressure induced reaction over another (see Table I).

2. *Explosions*—Experiments with organic compounds have confirmed observations of Bridgman.[2] We confirmed Professor Bridgman's findings that many organic compounds explode when subjected simultaneously to high pressure and high shear rates. Dr. A. J. Darnell did this work. Although we have published nothing formally on it, for the observations are incomplete, they were complete enough to show the types of general trend that sketch out what appears to be the general outlines of the high pressure chemistry of organic compounds. This is following on work of Dr. Irving Bengelsdorf who worked at the General Electric Laboratory with Dr. Tracy Hall and did a variety of high pressure exploratory experiments.[3] Of course it is necessary to point out that there has been a great deal of high pressure chemistry work in the range below 10 kb. This is described carefully and extremely well in Hamann's book.[4] In general, our work at UCLA in high pressures is carried out above this range, although a good part of the organic, as in the case of T-4 phage Coliphage, was done in this range. As Bengelsdorf has shown before, we found also that nearly all organic compounds undergo changes of one sort or another when subjected to pressures above 20 kb. In particular, explosions occur, polymerizations, and dramatic transformations. Bengelsdorf's technique had been to seal sample compounds in lead capsules and subject them to pressures. In doing so he polymerized acetone to make a yellow solid at 30 to 50 kb. and at temperatures around 300°C. Similar experiments with crotonaldehyde lead to no results, whereas paraldahyde at the lower temperature of 50°C always gave yellow polymers, highly insoluble, even in boiling decaline at 190°C. Methyl alcohol

TABLE I

	% of total with normal morphology	% of total with contracted sheath	% of phage with contracted sheath which have:		% total with empty heads and normal sheath	sample size
			full heads	empty heads		
control	95%	1%	less than 1%	100%	4%	297
0.25 min.	67 (46)	28	26	74	5	82
5.0 min.	10 (4)	80	11	89	less than 1	180
6°C	less than 1 (less than 1)	100	58	42	less than 1	173
25°C	10 (4)	80	11	89	less than 1	180
30°C	41 (3)	59	10	90	less than 1	135
45°C	less than 1 (less than 1)	100	5	95	less than 1	161

at 30 kb. and 370° exploded apparently giving ethylene. Our experiments were done mainly with pure hydrocarbons, either branched or straight chain saturated aliphatics. The general result was that we could not cause explosions in the case of the straight chain, but in the case of the branched chain it was possible to do this reproducibly whenever both shear and pressure were applied in the general range of 50 kb. Trapping of the gas lead to quite clear evidence of methane and olefins so it seems likely that the chemical change involved in the explosions of branched polyethylene under the conditions of pressure and shear is a formation of methane and olefins with energy evolution because of the relatively great stability of methane. On this basis one can see why the straight chain hydrocarbon does not explode.

Hardly more than exploratory experiments were done in this field, but the indications are that the area is a rich one.

3. *Pressure Cooking*—As a matter of general interest experiments were done with food stuffs. Bridgman had remarked[2] that egg white albumen could be coagulated by pressure.

Our experience fully collaborated this report, 10 kb. for five minutes at room temperature resulted in fully coagulated white gelatinous solid cooked egg white which had no odor, and tasted very similarly to ordinary cooked egg white. Similar results occurred in one minute. Similarly, egg yolks were cooked. There was an interesting difference here in that they were translucent; they also had no odor and did not color silver surfaces. It would appear that the sulphur-sulphur linkage involved in egg yolk proteins was not ruptured. Various other foods were cooked in this manner and eaten. For example, hamburger was cooked at 10 kb. for ten minutes at 20°. The results were no odor and it tasted well done. However, it did not taste like regularly cooked meat, although since the sample was at room temperature this might have been a factor. In general, our experience with the effects of pressures on foods would be that like that with the Coliphage, the probable effect was an uncoiling of protein helices through the breaking of hydrogen bonds, and that the applications of pressures at the range of 10 kb. at room temperatures has this effect, and will not break even sulphur-sulphur linkages and probably the weakest of the true chemical bonds. This could be a powerful tool in synthesis and analysis of complex organic and biochemical structures.

In summary, the whole field of high pressure organic chemistry appears to be a very rich one, and deserving of much more attention in the pressure range above 10 kb.

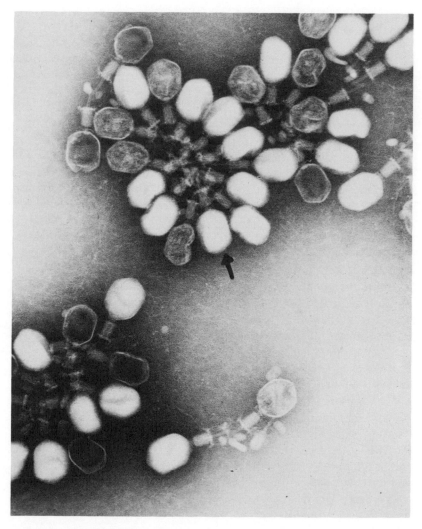

FIGURE 3. Sample pressurized at 6°C. Shows high proportion of phage with contracted sheaths and full heads.

B. Artificial Metals

Dr. A. J. Darnell has worked on the problem of artificial metals; the production of metals by application of pressures to non-metals followed by quenching to liquid nitorgen temperatures in order to

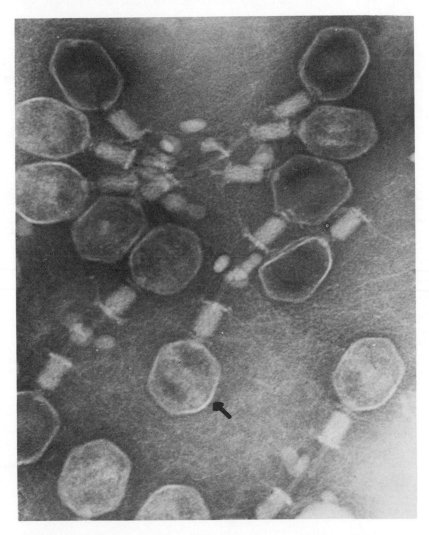

Figure 4. Sample pressurized at 25°C. Shows high proportion of phage with contracted sheaths and DNA released.

preserve the metastable phases for experimental laboratory investigations. In this way a number of new materials have been produced, among them metallic indium antimonide and its alloys with tin. Since this work other laboratories have produced numerous other examples, in particular, gallium. In general, one feels certain that the artificial metals offer great opportunity for solid state physics and

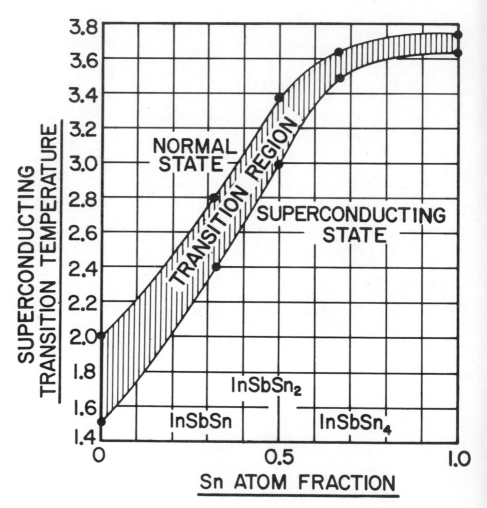

FIGURE 5. Superconducting transition temperature versus tin atom fraction for the InSb-Sn system.

chemistry. It seems clear that it will be possible, using the new techniques, to develop new metals almost at will thus varying parameters of great interest to the theory of metals and the solid state in general. In particular, we believe that superconductivity can be elucidated by this technique, and that features now obscure in the nature of superconductivity can be brought to light. For example, the indum antimonide tin alloys show us the variation of superconductivity transition temperatures with composition. This, despite the fact that the lattice constant and the geometry of the lattices as seen by the x-rays (which cannot distinguish between indium tin and antimony atoms), were constant to high precision throughout the series. Figure 5 shows that the strength of these materials varies smoothly, the diatomic compound being harder, as shown in Figure 6. It would seem on the basis of this that the alternating kernel charge which must be characteristic of indium antimonide

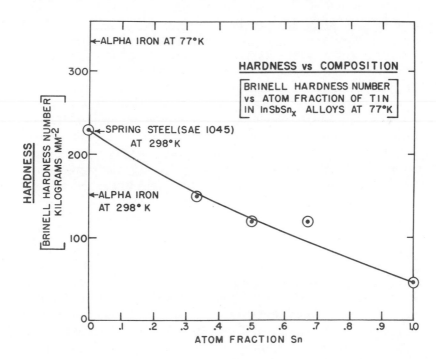

Figure 6. Brinell hardness numbers of the metallic alloy system InSb-Sn at 197°C.

probably imparts the hardness. Confirmatory experiments were done in the non-metallic diamond lattice phase by showing that the non-metallic tin was indeed softer than the non-metallic diamond lattice indium antimonide. Now, on this basis, we predict that the diamond form of boron nitride is much harder than diamond. Crystals of adequate size have not been available to test this important point. This, however, is a point of some possible general importance.

The freezing technique is one that has been useful not only in studying metals, but also other structures. In fact, it would be in this way that the combination of annealing and freezing by quenching with liquid nitrogen could make high pressure chemistry far more fruitful. In particular, Kamb and Davis[5] have isolated the densest form of ice and have shown its crystaline structure corresponded to essentially the closest packing of oxygen, although it did expand somewhat on release of the pressure. Similarly, Kasper and Brandhorst[6] found a new structure of metallic indium antimonide at around 30 kb which can be derived from the simple beta-tin structure which appears at 23 kb by a simple shear process. It appears that this structure reverts to the beta-tin structure on release of pressure even though the quenching to 77°K has been carried out. Thus we see some evidence of structures that cannot be quenched, or at least of some structures that can be more easily quenched than others. So one must proceed with some caution about planning for quenching of high pressure metastable structures. However, in general, the technique is a very fruitful one, and we believe that there are many, many applications remaining. In fact, our plans during the next years include considerable further work in the general area of the artificial metals; investigating in particular the effects of structural and valence electron differences on the properties of metals, e.g. strength, electrical conductivity, superconductivity, color, velocity of sound, and so on. This work will be pursued in conjunction with Professor Hans Bömmel's group in Physics and Professor George Kennedy's and Professor David Griggs' groups in the Institute of Geophysics. We have developed a Crystal-Growing Laboratory which has as its principal purpose the production of crystals for research study. A very modern high pressure press has been installed together with facilities for quenching under the high pressure conditions. In this connection it has been our experience that the piston and cylinder apparatus allows quenching more readily than other designs. In the design of high pressure apparatus it is important, if the quenching technique is to be used, to consider the possibility of getting the liquid nitrogen effectively to the sample while it is under the high pressure.

A general result of some interest has been reported by Musgrave.[7] He reports that the work of compression (PΔV), the pressure at the transition from the non-metallic phase multiplied by the volume change, gives a value equal to one half of the electronic energy gap in the non-metallic diamond form. For obscure reasons this regularity seems to be particularly good for the Group IV elements, silicon and germanium, and to work quite well for indium antimonide, the numbers being 51.6% for silicon, 52.0% for germanium, and 57.0% for indium antimonide. On this basis, it is possible to estimate the pressure required to make metallic diamond out of diamond using the energy gap; it would appear that something in the neighborhood of at least one million atmospheres, one megabar, would be needed. In fact, the rigorous calculations would give something in excess of two megabars. Thus it would seem that it will be a long time before laboratory techniques for making metallic diamond will suffice. Nevertheless, there is little doubt that pressures in the vicinity of one megabar would open up a whole new world of chemical and physical phenomenon. In Drickamer's laboratory in Illinois, small samples have been carried to the vicinity of half a megabar with the result that a large number of transformations, changes in electrical resistivity, and optical properties have been observed. No quenching has been attempted at these pressures and the samples are so small that it would be difficult to do many experiments even if the structures were retainable by quenching. Thus there is a very large instrument design problem, an engineering problem, for the laboratory apparatus which will allow a sample of some volume, say one cubic centimeter, to be compressed to megabar pressures to be designed and built. The highest priority should be given to any leads for this design. We take hope from the finding that diamond probably is stable to compressional transitions for pressures well above one megabar. It may be the magic material needed for the parts. The machining may be possible with diamond boron nitride.

II   RADIATION CHEMISTRY

A.   Positive Ion Chemistry

1. *High yield of heavy molecular weight hydrocarbon by ionization of methane*—It has been shown[8] during the last few months that the gamma ray exposure of both solid and gaseous methane leads to the production of high molecular weight hydrocarbons, very highly branched, in high yield (G is approximately 1 for methane loss and conversion into heavy hydrocarbons). Earlier work had established that the irradiation of gaseous methane by ionizing radiations caused polymer to form. This work, however, having been done in the gas phase, perhaps left some doubt as to the broad nature of the chemistry. At the present time, we believe it is quite clear that the chemistry is not due to free radicals, but is most likely due to ions. We have investigated this reaction carefully and established some of the effect of electron transfer and thus have given good evidence for the positive ion nature of the chemistry, it being clear that quenching by substances of lower ionization potential is some proof of positive ions.

On the basis of this work, we expect that the ionizing ultraviolet radiation bombarding reducing planetary atmospheres produces high molecular weight hydrocarbons and it is conceivable that part of the present crude oil had its origin in this mechanism. It is interesting to speculate about the nature of the reaction products on Jupiter.

2. *Electron transfer to put charge on species of lowest ionization potential*—Experiments with solutions of hexane in liquid xenon have shown conclusively that when ionization of either molecule takes place the positive charge ultimately reaches the solute hexane because of its lower ionization potential. Thus we see that it is very likely that the radiation chemistry of ionizing radiation will concentrate in the species of lowest ionization potential. This general conclusion is one of extreme importance in the chemistry of planetary atmospheres. We thus can see that the ionizing energy incident on the atmospheres may be concentrated in certain species and thus be directed to their chemical reactions.

3. *Ionizing ultraviolet in sunlight and probable effects on planetary atmospheres like Jupiter's*—A powerful helium light source has been made[9] by producing a low voltage helium plasma. With this we have investigated the effects of this ionizing ultraviolet light on

methane and found them to be very similar to those observed[8] with cobalt 60 gamma rays. With this result we predict that the ionizing ultraviolet in the sunlight must have appreciable effects on reducing planetary atmospheres, wherever they may have occurred. The consequences, of course, may be that heavy hydrocarbons are very common constituents of planets and that in particular, some of the earth's petroleum may have had this origin.

4. *General laws of positive ion chemistry*—One comprehensive paper has been published[10] and further general thoughts and general conclusions were stated at the Gordon Conference in July of 1964. It appears to be entirely possible to write down general laws for the chemistry of positive ions and that these laws can be extremely helpful in guiding experiments and interpreting the results for ionic radiation chemistry. For example, it appears that the principle of analogy is very valid, and that an electronic structure which is charged will have chemical properties which are very similar to those of the neutral structure with the same number of electrons. Thus A^+ is much like chlorine in its chemistry. Also, there are new features such as an electron exchange binding between identical systems or systems which have not had time to become different in shape. This constitutes an adhesive force additional to that due to electronic polarization and helps bind the positive ion to the neutral molecule until it has had a chance to react electronically by the normal processes of the filling of valence orbitals.

One should expect also that the phenomenon of ionic relaxation is very fundamental to positive ion chemistry. After an ion is formed it naturally wishes to assume a different and new geometry; this takes time. In condensed systems, the chemical reactions may occur before the relaxation. After relaxation has occurred, such effects as electronic exchange bindings are forbidden by the Franck-Condon Principle, and the consequences are that the chemical effects in dilute systems in the gas phase should be quite different from those in the solid.

5. *Possible applications*—The enormous quantity of ionizing radition which is available in atomic power reactors makes conceivable possible practical applications of positive ion chemistry. If we should come to understand it sufficiently well, it might just be possible to produce economically chemicals that have substantial value on the

present market and thus to create a new chemical industry and a new use for atomic energy.

In any case, the studies of positive ion chemistry will be enlightening for the effects of radiation on living tissue in causing mutations and cancer and their bearing on the understanding of the planetary atmosphere chemistry and the effects that these ionizing radiations may have had in times past on the earth. It appears more than likely, also, that chemical reactions are of real importance in plasmas such as those involved in the Sherwood Project to tame thermo-nuclear energy.

This work on radiation has been done by Dr. Larry Kevan, now at the University of Chicago, shortly to move to the University of Kansas; Dr. Carl Jensen, and Dr. Donald Davis.

B.   Hot Atom Chemistry

The chemical effects of nuclear transmutation are very interesting and have considerable significance for the use of x-rays and other energetic radiations in exciting chemical reactions. In particular, Dr. Armen Kazanjian has studied the nature of the isomeric transition in Bromine 80, and the reason that its chemical effects appear to be essentially identical in many systems with those of straight recoil caused by emission of gamma rays from thermal neutron capture.

1. *Isomeric transition vs. (n, γ) chemistry*—We have been studying the hot atom chemistry of bromine atoms, produced on the one hand by the capture of thermal neutrons followed by the subsequent emission of energetic gamma rays the so-called (n, γ) process, and on the other hand by the isomeric transition, the process by which a gamma ray transition from the 4.5 hour excited state of Br^{80} to the lower 18 minute state of Br^{80} occurs with the emission of a K electron. The direct emission of the gamma ray without internal conversion in the innermost electronic shell of the Br atom is extremely improbable. Following the internal conversion transition, the positive charge is increased further by the Auger process, by which instead of the emission of x-rays to fill the vacancy in the K-shell, two vacancies appear in the L-shell resulting from the dropping of an electron from the atom, resulting in net $+2$ charge. This continues through the M-shells and so on and can lead to as many as a $+12$ charge on the Br atom. This, of course, causes the mole-

cule, in which the Br atom was bound before the isomeric transition occurred, to disintegrate. Also the daughter Br^{80}, which itself is radioactive with a half life of 18 minutes to form Kr^{80} is freed in the solution. Dr. Kazanjian has been studying its reactions in various organic media, in particular, propyl bromide, in both the normal and iso forms. It has been known for many years that the products produced by the (n, γ) and the isomeric process were strangely similar, and we have shown in detail that they are similar under a wide variety of conditions. We have just discovered the reason for this exact similarity.

It appears that because of the large electron affinity of the highly-charged Br atom, electrons are captured by it from the immediate environment, and in particular from other portions of the same molecule, say propyl bromide, in which the four and a half hour Br^{80} was held, thus putting positive charge over the molecule as a whole. This causes the organic bromide molecule to fission resulting in the Br ion and organic ions flying apart with energies of expulsion approaching those due to the (n, γ) recoil. By simple calculation it is possible to show that energies of ten electron volts or more for the Br atom are not unreasonable, and it seems very likely that the bond between the carbon and Br will rupture preferentially when one realizes that most likely the largest charge force will lie between the bromine ion and the residual charged organic radical. It is well known that as a consequence of the higher electron affinity of Br^+ ions when traveling with the velocity of a few electron volts energy, they will capture electrons from the immediate environment to form neutral atoms. Thus we have the Br^{80} daughter traveling with some 10 electron volts as a neutral atom. This is exactly the conditon we envisage as being characteristic of the (n, γ) process, where the gamma ray recoil usually produces energy of 100 electron volts at most, and many data indicate that a majority of the reactions in hot atom chemistry occur near the end of the range where the energy probably does not exceed a few electron volts. Thus we see that the isomeric and (n, γ) processes should be essentially identical in their chemical effects for media in which the electron affinity of Br^+ is greater than the ionization potential of the medium. In media with the ionization potential greater than the electron affinity of Br^+ we should expect to find that the hot atom chemistry of the (n, γ) process would differ radically from the hot atom chemistry of the isomeric process. Such results were found and are given in Table II; they show the expected large difference for the CF_3Br system in which the ionization potential of 12.3 volts is above that of atomic bromine, 11.8 volts.

2. *C^{14} Hot Atom Chemistry*—The chemistry of energetic recoil carbon atoms has been studied now for some time in our group and we have joined others in concluding that most of the hot atom chemistry of carbon is occurring near the thermal range. Therefore, in an attempt to test what the truly thermal reactions are, we performed experiments with carbon atoms evaporated from a carbon rod. These results are extremely interesting in that they show that the evaporation of carbon atoms onto cold benzene cooled in liquid nitrogen causes the formation of toluene and cycloheptatriene as shown in Table II.

III   HIGH TEMPERATURE CHEMISTRY

Our achievements in this area consist solely of the construction of three plasma torches, one of which goes to the power of half a megawatt. With these facilities we expect to reach temperatures of 100,000° with nearly all gases and to be able to do considerable work in the very, very high temperature range.

Present models have a design capability of 70,000°F, corresponding to the surface temperature of the hottest known star, roughly ten times hotter than the surface of the sun.

The light emitted by stars ranges over the entire spectrum—from the far ultraviolet through the visible to the far infrared. Much of this radiation is absorbed in the upper layers of the Earth's atmosphere, and is lost to observation. Radiation in the visible range, however, is not appreciably absorbed, and has long provided information about the composition and temperature of the stars through spectroscopic techniques.

While elements present in a star could be identified, accurate measurements were not possible of their relative quantities. Comparison spectra were necessary from plasmas of known composition, at the temperature of the star studied. Our plasma torches are now providing uncontaminated spectra of gases whose composition may be varied with accuracy. These spectra may now be compared to solar and stellar spectra obtaned astronomically. Furthermore, the

TABLE II

SUMMARY OF RESULTS

Run No.	1	2	3	4	5	6	7
Rod Temp. (°K)[a]	1893	2122	2225	2253	2320	2353	2390
Rod Surface Area (cm²)	7.5	6.6	6.6	7.5	6.6	7.5	6.9
Carbon Evap. Rate (g/cm²sec.)[b]	3.3×10^{-13}	8.4×10^{-11}	2.3×10^{-10}	2.3×10^{-9}	8.8×10^{-9}	1.6×10^{-8}	3.5×10^{-8}
Total Carbon Evaporated (g)	8.9×10^{-9}	2.0×10^{-6}	1.8×10^{-5}	6.2×10^{-5}	2.1×10^{-4}	4.3×10^{-4}	8.7×10^{-4}
Concn. Identified Products (M)[c] Toluene	d	d	2.1×10^{-5}	4.9×10^{-5}	1.1×10^{-4}	d	d
Cycloheptatriene	d	d	app. 2×10^{-5e}	8.6×10^{-4}	4.2×10^{-5}	d	d

[a] Measured by optical pyrometry.

[b] The carbon evaporation rate data used were from the work of M. Hock, P. Blackburn, D. Dingledy and H. Johnston, *J. Phys. Chem.*, *59*, 97(1955).

[c] Product yields were determined by comparison of peak heights to peak heights from standards; peak heights for toluene and cycloheptatriene are linear in concentration over the concentration range 3×10^{-1} to 3×10^{-5} *M*.

[d] Product yield was less than the limits of detection, which are 8.8×10^{-6} *M* for toluene and 1.8×10^{-5} *M* for cycloheptatriene for 2 μ 1 injections.

[e] This yield was just barely above the limit of detection.

simulated spectra provide information in the nonvisible range absorbed by the Earth's atmosphere.

During the 131st Annual Meeting of the American Association for the Advancement of Science held last December 26 through December 30 in Montreal, Canada, our AFOSR Exhibit offered us an opportunity to demonstrate our techniques with the plasma torch.

This exhibit demonstrated the research the AFOSR is sponsoring in our Space Chemistry Program at UCLA. In the demonstration, artificial metals were created from nonmetallic matter under pressures of 40,000 atmospheres, and were quenched by cooling with liquid nitrogen. These new metals remained in the metallic state when the pressure was removed, permitting investigation of such properties as superconductivity and crystal structure. The process of cooking foods under pressure without heat was also shown, and other portions of our exhibit described the effects of ionizing radiation on methane gas to produce lubricating oil, and the transfer of energy from ions of higher ionization potential to methane by electron transfer.

The following pictures are from this exhibit. Picture 1 shows the entire exhibit. Picture 2 a side view of the plasma torch, demonstrating the lighting technique. Picture 3 shows the oscillator section of the plasma torch being used as a light source with a spectrograph in order to study the nature of the emitting sources in the plasma. Picture 4 is a close-up of the plasma of Picture 3 plasma torch in operation at one atmosphere, using Argon plasma gas with a power level in the plasma at approximately 5 kilowatts.

IV   HIGH VACUUM CHEMISTRY

No facilities or progress have been made as yet in this area. It is hoped that a graduate student will join us shortly to take on this general assignment.

REFERENCES

[1] Nemethy and Scherago (1962) *J. Chem. Phys., 36,* p. 3401.

[2] P. W. Bridgman (1958) *The Physics of High Pressures,* London: G. Bell and Sons.

[3] Private communication.

[4] S. D. Hamann (1957) *Physical Chemical Effects of Pressure,* New York: Interscience Publishers.

[5] A. J. Darnell and W. F. Libby (1964) *Phys. Rev., 135,* p. A1453.

[6] B. R. Tittmann, A. J. Darnell, H. E. Bömmell, and W. F. Libby (1964), *Phys. Rev., 135*, p. A1460.

[7] A. J. Darnell and W. F. Libby, (1965) *Progress in Solid State Chemistry, 2,* p. 1.

[8] W. B. Kamb and D. L. Davis (1964) *Science, 144* p. 991.

[9] J. S. Kasper and H. Brandhorst (1964) *Journal of Chem. Phys., 41,* p. 3768.

[10] M. J. P. Musgrave (1964) *Proceedings of Physical Society, 84,* p. 585.

[11] D. R. Davis and W. F. Libby (1964) *Science, 144,* p. 991.

[12] C. A. Jensen and W. F. Libby (1964) *Phys. Rev., 135,* p. A1247.

[13] W. F. Libby (1961) *J. Chem. Phys., 35,* No. 5, p. 1714.

PICTURE 1. The AFOSR-UCLA Space Chemistry Exhibit at the 131st Annual Meeting of the American Association for the Advancement of Science. December 26 - 30, 1964, in Montreal, Canada.

PICTURE 2. Side view of the plasma torch—demonstrating of the lighting technique.

PICTURE 3. The oscillator section of the plasma torch being used as a light source with a spectrograph in order to study the nature of the emitting sources in the plasma.

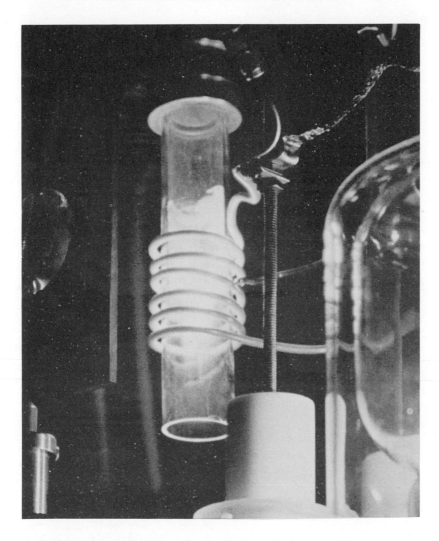

PICTURE 4. A close up of the plasma of Picture 3 plasma torch in operation at one atmosphere using Argon plasma gas with a power level in the plasma at approximately 5 kilowatts.

XV. The Nature of the Long-Range Interaction in Hemoglobin

WILLARD F. LIBBY

IT IS SUGGESTED that the well known strong interaction (2.3 kcal/mole) at long distances (25 Å) occurring between the iron porphyrins (hemes in hemoglobin) is due most probably to induced dipole Van der Waal's forces between the iron porphyrin platelets which are highly polarizable in the unoxygenated state, and much less so in oxyhemoglobin. The orientations of the vector normals of the two closest heme pairs for the four hemes in horse oxyhemoglobin are nearly, but not perfectly, correct for an interaction of this type. The interaction would be increased to a maximum by an 11.5° rotation of two platelets and a 16° rotation of the other two. This structure should apply to hemoglobin for which the platelet orientations are unknown at present. Muirhead and Perutz, however, report a structural change to occur when hemoglobin is oxygenated. We suggest that this consists in part of the small platelet rotations mentioned. Perutz and Mazzarella report also that Hemoglobin H, which shows no interaction for reasons involving other points (mentioned later) shows no crystal structure change on oxygenation.

It is proposed that the difference in the polarizabilities probably is due to two extra resonating (pi) electrons in the porphyrin plane existing in hemoglobin, the hole in the center of the porphyrin defined by the four nitrogen atoms being bridged by the two iron valence electrons which make resonating sigma bonds to the four nitrogen atoms. This assignment leaves the four nitrogen atoms equivalent and gives it $26 + 2x$ pi electrons where x is the number of pi electrons contributed by the two vinyl groups depending on the degree of coplanarity with the porphyrin ring, x being 2 for complete coplanarity. The two unshared pairs of the sigma bonded nitrogens are forced into the pi system. In oxyhemoglobin, only 24 pi electrons occur because the iron atom, being diamagnetic, is necessarily in six-fold octahedral coordination with the four planar nitrogens, each of which must contribute an unshared pair of electrons (together with the nitrogen of the histidine below the plane, and the oxygen [made diamagnetic with the two iron valence electrons] lying above the plane).

The iron is free to sit above or below the plane in hemoglobin, in our theory, in agreement with some observations. It must, however, be coplanar in oxyhemoglobin, apparently in agreement with observation.

It is suggested that the vinyl chains with their four additional pi electrons give the requisite polarizability which, with the hypothetical perfect platelet orientations predicted for human hemoglobin and unit dielectric constant, is 2360 Å^3. However, the calculation of the polarizability is so difficult that it has not been completed. If the two vinyl side chains are omitted the calculation gives no large polarizability to the free electron network molecular orbital approximation. Our theory thus predicts the vinyl side chains in hemoglobin to be necessary for the heme heme interaction and to be coplanar with the heme plane to promote the pi resonance. In oxyhemoglobin, the vinyl groups need not be coplanar.

The requisite polarizability together with the drop on oxygenation appears to follow theoretically for an x value of 1, i.e. only partially coplanar vinyls. The strong interaction between the four iron porphyrin groups in hemoglobin relative to oxyhemoglobin reduces its affinity for oxygen as compared to the analogous system, myoglobin, which has only one iron porphyrin. In fact, taking dilute myoglobin solutions as the base for the expected interaction-free behavior of hemoglobin or using the detailed shape of the oxygenation curve for hemoglobin, a single value of the planar polarizability for the porphyrin system in hemoglobin fits the experimental oxygen saturation curve satisfactorily. Thus our theory gives a single parameter, the polarizability, with which the oxygenation curve can be fitted once the structure of the hemoglobin molecule is known.

The preponderance of the many experimental observations on the hemoglobins, oxyhemoglobins, myglobins, and oxymyoglobins appear to fit the theory either directly or indirectly. Among these are:

1. The Bohr Effect—the decreased strength of the protein acids and bases on oxygenation, and the reduction of the heme heme interaction (judged by the oxygen uptake curve) in strongly basic

solutions (probably in acidic also). This is explained by the acidic and basic side groups on the polypeptide chains wrapped around the porphyrin platelets, two (the α chains) containing 16 acidic and 24 basic groups and the other two (the β chains) containing 24 and 23, respectively, become electrostatically charged as the pH is shifted. This, due to the low dielectric constant of the proteinaceous matter constituting the main central part of the hemoglobin molecule, causes the chains and the platelets to be pushed apart against the interaction in a kind of swelling effect. The weak positive ions are neutralized at pH values above the isoelectric point leaving a net negative charge on the chains and repulsion. The opposite process occurs with pH values below the isoelectric point. Thus the neutralization free energy for the bases in high pH in hemoglobin (and for the acids in low pH) must be less by the amount of the work done against the heme heme interaction forces in the swelling, and the dissociation constants of both the acids and bases in hemoglobin are increased relative to the values in oxyhemoglobin.

2. The detailed fit of the individual equilibrium constants K_1, K_2, K_3, and K_4 for the oxygenation of the four hemes in hemoglobin and the independence of K_4 of the nature of the substituents on the first three hemes (whether they be CO or other molecules different from O_2). The ratios of the K's are given uniquely by our one-parameter theory and the agreement of the individual K's attests to the close fit of the oxygenation curve. The observed independence of K_4 of the nature of the first three inactivating ligands is due to the complete elimination of the interaction, in our theory, by inactivation of the first three hemes.

3. The fact that dissociation to the diheme has little effect on the oxygen uptake curve. The relatively great strength of the interaction between the closest and most properly oriented heme pairs (the hemes, one with an α chain and the other with a β chain) means that the total interaction is reduced relatively little by splitting the molecule into diheme systems consisting of one α and one β polypeptide chain each. It is a prediction of our theory that the splitting occurs in this particular way. The evidence seems to favor this.

4. The fact that the oxygenation curve for myoglobin is independent of pH (no Bohr Effect). The absence of heme heme interaction in dilute myoglobin requires that no Bohr Effect exists, according to our theory.

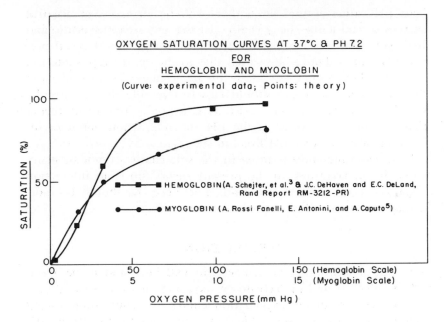

FIGURE 1

5. The essentiality of the vinyl side chains to the interaction. The polarizability probably is due, in significant part, to the vinyl side chains contributing four additional pi electrons. This requires that the vinyl side chains be coplanar with the porphyrin in hemoglobin, although not in oxyhemoglobin.

6. The decrease of the oxygen affinity of hemoglobin in concentrated solutions. Since our theory uses a Van der Waal's interaction, the interactions are non-saturable and the interactions with three other hemes within the molecule in no way, except possibly in angular orientation and in distance of separation, inhibits a heme in interacting with hemes in neighboring molecules. Therefore, concentrated hemoglobin solutions have their oxygen affinities further reduced by the intermolecular interactions between hemes.

7. The fact that Hemoglobin H, the hemoglobin form with four β chains instead of the usual two, shows no interaction. The β chains have essentially ten excess acidic side groups, including the ends (because the histidine basic side chain is so weak) so at normal

body pH values around seven there will be an excess of negative charges spread along the β chain. (In the α chains, the acidic and basic side chains nearly balance.) Thus Hemoglobin H at all normal pH values should be swollen due to the charge repulsion and therefore should show essentially no heme heme interactions, and the oxygen uptake curve should closely resemble that of myoglobin. No Bohr Effect should exist. It is a prediction of our theory that at some lower value of the pH the interaction might occur. This might be between pH five and six.

8. Species differences residing in the side chains cannot be manifested in K_4 according to the present theory since no interaction remains for the final O_2 addition. Therefore, K_4 should be independent of species. This seems to be true.

PREDICTIONS

1. The polarizability of hemoglobin will be found to be about 3000 to 4000 $Å^3$ and to decrease on oxygenation by at least 90%.

2. Differences in the oxygenation curves for hemoglobin among different species and under different conditions (temperature, pH, salt concentrations) depend mainly on the geometrical arrangement of the heme platelets and the acid base equilibrium of the constituent amino acids in the polypeptide chains. The geometrical arrangement of the chains is important through the effect it has on the interactions between the charges developed by acid base dissociation and neutralization.

3. Met hemoglobin (hemoglobin with $+3$ iron, oxidation having removed one 3d electron) will have an interaction between hemes of about the same magnitude as that found in hemoglobin.

4. All ligands will interact more energetically with and be bound more firmly to myoglobin than hemoglobin, the difference being the interaction discussed here.

5. Crystalline human hemoglobin will show the porphyrin platelets to have normals lying in the a, b plane of the crystal with the normals at the angles given.

6. The location of the two vinyl side groups in positions 2 and 4 of the porphyrin will be found to maximize the polarizability. (These quantum mechanical calulations are now underway with R. Shafer.)

7. Although the iron atom in hemoglobin need not be coplanar with the porphyrin, it will be coplanar in the oxyhemoglobins.

8. The ratios of the K's will be independent of the ligands used.

9. The constant K_4 will depend on the overall concentration of hemoglobin due to heme heme intermolecular interaction, decreasing with increasing concentration.

10. Hemoglobin H in the more acidic pH range, possibly between 5 and 6, will show decreased oxygen affinity and appreciable sensitivity to pH (Bohr Effect).

CONCLUSION

The oxygenation of hemoglobin as affected by the heme heme interaction apparently can be explained by a very long range Van der Waal's electronic polarizability interaction much stronger for hemoglobin than for oxyhemoglobin due to the electronic level structures of the pi electrons in the porphyrin system, hemoglobin having two more pi electrons. The quantum theoretical calculations given merely show that such an explanation is possible theoretically. The fact that the particular molecular orbital treatment used gives about the polarizabilities required may be somewhat fortuitous and the quantum theoretical calculations probably should be taken merely as being permissive in that they show a Van der Waal's type of interaction to be entirely conceivable, and not in violation of the quantum theory.

Experimentally, the evidence, varied and detailed as it is, seems to fit the theory with a pi electron polarizability of about $4000 \cdot 10^{-24}$ cubic centimeters in hemoglobin and with a much smaller polarizability of the pi electron system in oxyhemoglobin. This seems to require that the two vinyl groups contribute and be coplanar with the heme platelets in hemoglobin. The Bohr Effect of acids and bases and the effects of added salt are in keeping with our theory in that charge repulsion causes a swelling and a rapid drop in the interaction with consequent increase in oxygen affinity. Species differences due to the location of acidic and basic amino acids on the protein chains are understandable because the sensitivity of the interaction to inter heme distances and platelet orientations would be so great.

ACKNOWLEDGMENTS

The author is very indebted to Mr. Allen Minton for the calculation of the F values by computer and for many helpful discussions; to Professor Edward Teller for help with the quantum theory, and to Professor F. J. W. Roughton for detailed information on the oxygenation equilibria of hemoglobin.